THERE GOES THE SHUTOUT

Peanuts Parade Paperbacks

1. Who's the Funny-Looking Kid with the Big Nose?
2. It's a Long Way to Tipperary
3. There's a Vulture Outside
4. What's Wrong with Being Crabby?
5. What Makes You Think You're Happy?
6. Fly, You Stupid Kite, Fly!
7. The Mad Punter Strikes Again
8. A Kiss on the Nose Turns Anger Aside
9. Thank Goodness for People
10. What Makes Musicians So Sarcastic?
11. Speak Softly, and Carry a Beagle
12. Don't Hassle Me with Your Sighs, Chuck
13. There Goes the Shutout
14. Always Stick Up for the Underbird
15. It's Hard Work Being Bitter
16. How Long, Great Pumpkin, How Long?

THERE GOES THE SHUTOUT

Cartoons from *More Peanuts* and *Good Grief, More Peanuts!*

by Charles M. Schulz

Holt, Rinehart and Winston / New York

Published simultaneously in Canada by Holt, Rinehart
and Winston of Canada, Limited.

First published in this form in 1977.

Library of Congress Catalog Card Number: 76-43499

ISBN: 0-03-020676-6

Printed in the United States of America

10 9 8 7 6 5 4 3 2 1

?
CLUMP
KLOMP
CLUMP
KLOMP

WHAT'S THAT?!
IT SOUNDS LIKE A HERD OF ELEPHANTS!
...OR A TANK BATTALION
?
?
?

THEY'RE COMING TOWARD US!
WE'RE TRAPPED!!
CLUMP
KLOMP
CLUMP
KLOMP

EVERY WINTER IT'S THE SAME THING...GIRLS IN STADIUM BOOTS!
KLUMP
CLUMP
KLUMP
KLUMP
CLOMP
CLUMP!
KLOMP!
SCHULZ

?
?!
SCHULZ

SIGH

HOW HUMILIATING!

WHAT'S THE MATTER WITH YOU?
I'VE BEEN DISGRACED FOR LIFE!

THEY SAY IT'S NEVER HAPPENED TO ANYONE BEFORE

I'VE JUST BEEN EXPELLED FROM NURSERY SCHOOL!
SCHULZ

IF THERE'S ANYTHING I CAN'T STAND, IT'S HAVING TO EAT BARE SOUP!!

BEAR SOUP?!

YEAH... THERE'S NOT A SINGLE CRACKER IN THE HOUSE...

SO I HAVE TO EAT BARE SOUP!
SCHULZ

HIC!
HIC!
HIC!
?

HEY, LUCY, YOUR BABY BROTHER'S GOT THE HICCUPS!

HE SHOULDN'T BE HICCUPING, SHOULD HE?
WHY NOT?

HIC! HIC! HIC!
HE HASN'T GOT ANYTHING ELSE TO DO!
SCHULZ

YAWN

MAN! THAT'S THE 'TIREDEST' DOG I'VE EVER KNOWN..
WHAT HAS HE GOT TO BE SO TIRED ABOUT?

HAVE YOU EVER BEEN A DOG?
OF COURSE NOT..

WELL, FROM WHAT I'VE HEARD, IT CAN BE VERY TIRESOME
SCHULZ

I WANT TO SHOW YOU MY NEW COMIC STRIP, SCHROEDER BECAUSE I THINK YOU'LL APPRECIATE IT..

THIS ONE MUSICIAN ASKS THE OTHER IF HE CAN PLAY THE 'HALLELUJAH CHORUS,' SEE? AND THIS GUY SAYS, 'OH, I GUESS I CAN HANDEL IT!'

GET IT? GET IT? PRETTY GOOD, HUH? HUH?!!

IT'S SORT OF SAD WHEN YOU THINK OF A KID LIKE THAT GOING THROUGH LIFE WITHOUT A SENSE OF HUMOR..
SCHULZ

WILL YOU MAKE ME A BREAD AN' BUDDER SAN'WICH, CHARLIE BROWN?
OH, GOOD GRIEF!

DON'T CUT IT! DON'T CUT IT!

THAT'S RIGHT...JUST FOLD IT OVER
SIGH

WHEN YOU CUT 'EM, THEY LOSE ALL THEIR FLAVOR!
SCHULZ

DO YOU KNOW WHY THE SUN IS ROUND, CHARLIE BROWN?

NO, I CAN'T SAY THAT I DO..
I THINK IT WOULD BE MORE PRACTICAL TO HAVE IT SHAPED LIKE A FLUORESCENT LIGHT..

I DON'T KNOW ABOUT THAT, BUT I DO KNOW ONE THING..
WHAT'S THAT?

IT'S TOO LATE TO CHANGE IT NOW!
SCHULZ

AC

YOU CAN'T WATCH TELEVISION FROM WAY BACK HERE, LINUS...MOVE UP WHERE YOU CAN SEE...

SCHULZ

SOB
SNIF SNIF

WHY IS YOUR BABY BROTHER CRYING? IS HE WATCHING A SAD PROGRAM?

NO...
CLICK!

HE JUST GETS DEPRESSED BECAUSE HE DOESN'T KNOW HOW TO TURN THE SET ON...
SIGH
SCHULZ

THAT SNOWMAN IS JUST AS MUCH MINE AS IT IS YOURS!

IN FACT, CHARLIE BROWN... IF YOU DON'T LOOK OUT, I'M JUST LIABLE TO TAKE MY HALF, AND GO HOME!
OH, HO-HO-HO! YOU WOULDN'T DARE!

WOULDN'T I?
UH UH!

SCHULZ

DO YOU REALIZE THAT THERE ARE ONLY 347 DAYS UNTIL CHRISTMAS?

DON'T I KNOW IT? AND NEW YEAR'S COMES RIGHT AFTER THAT

IT JUST DOESN'T SEEM POSSIBLE

I DON'T KNOW WHERE THE TIME GOES...
SCHULZ

HELLO,.. SCHROEDER? I CALLED TO INVITE YOU TO MY PARTY...

I WAS WONDERING IF YOU'D BRING YOUR PIANO, AND PLAY FOR US...YOU WILL? GOOD...

I'VE ALSO INVITED A FELLOW WHO PLAYS THE ACCORDION, AND I'M SURE YOU AND HE...

HELLO? HELLO?
SCHULZ

YOU DON'T LIKE ME!

THAT'S ALWAYS BEEN THE WHOLE TROUBLE...
YOU JUST DON'T LIKE ME!!

SURE, I DO, CHARLIE BROWN...I LIKE YOU.. REALLY I DO...
WELL, MAYBE YOU LIKE ME A LITTLE...

BUT I KNOW YOU DON'T THINK I'M PERFECT!
SCHULZ

LOOK...TWO GLASSES OF WATER PERFECTLY BALANCED

WELL, IF THAT ISN'T THE SILLIEST THING I'VE EVER SEEN!
!
?

HOW ANYONE CAN SIT AROUND BALANCING THINGS ON HIS EARS WITH ALL THE TROUBLE THERE IS IN THE WORLD TODAY....WELL,...I JUST DON'T KNOW..

SCHULZ

HEY, SNOOPY, HOW ABOUT GOING FOR A WALK?

SCHULZ
WALKS ARE KIND OF RELAXING, BUT THE PRELIMINARIES DRIVE ME CRAZY!

YOU'LL NEVER GUESS WHAT I GOT YOU FOR YOUR BIRTHDAY...

IN FACT, I DON'T THINK YOU COULD GUESS IN A MILLION YEARS!

YOU'D NEVER GUESS IN A MILLION BILLION YEARS!
A JUMPING ROPE!

SCHULZ

OLD-FASHIONED! NO IMAGINATION!

TRITE! VERY TRITE!

I DON'T KNOW WHAT'S WRONG WITH THE KIDS IN THIS NEIGHBORHOOD...

SCHULZ

WELL, YOU LOOK WARM, CHARLIE BROWN...

OH, I AM...YES, SIR..I BELIEVE IN BEING PREPARED FOR COLD WEATHER

THERE'S ONLY ONE THING WRONG..
WHAT'S THAT?

I CAN'T MOVE!
SCHULZ

PLOP
!

DON'T BE MAD....YOU'RE THE FIRST PERSON I'VE HIT TODAY!
SCHULZ

Charlie Brown

Charlie Brown

lie
wn
SCHULZ

Schroeder

I'M NOT GOING TO SCHOOL TODAY, CHARLIE BROWN..

WHAT'S THE OCCASION THIS TIME? IT COULDN'T BE BEETHOVEN'S BIRTHDAY AGAIN SO SOON, COULD IT?

I SUPPOSE IT'S BACH'S BIRTHDAY? OR IS IT SCHUBERT'S? OR BRAHMS'? OR TSCHAIKOVSKY'S? OR HAYDN'S?

NOPE...MINE!
SCHULZ

EVERYBODY THAT I KNOW HAS SEEN THAT NEW 3-D MOVIE

EVERYBODY?

UH, HUH...EVERYBODY
SCHULZ

WHAT IN THE WORLD ARE **YOU** DOING?

I'M COUNTING THE STARS..
HOW MANY ARE THERE?

OH, GEE....I WOULDN'T HAVE ANY IDEA..

I'M JUST COUNTING THEM..I DON'T TRY TO KEEP TRACK
SCHULZ

WHEN YOU GET MARRIED, YOU HAVE TO CHANGE YOUR NAME, DON'T YOU?

YES, I GUESS YOU DO...
MRS. CHARLIE BROWN...

MRS. GOOD OL' CHARLIE BROWN...

NOPE,..I JUST CAN'T SEE IT!
SCHULZ

SCHULZ

MOTHER'S TRYING TO GET LINUS TO EAT BY HIMSELF..

IF HE KNOCKS HIS DISH OFF THE TABLE THREE TIMES, HE HAS TO GO TO BED WITHOUT ANY SUPPER

IS THAT TEACHING HIM TO EAT?

NO, BUT IT'S TAUGHT HIM TO COUNT TO THREE!
SCHULZ

WE'RE GOING TO HAVE A PARTY AND WE'RE **NOT** GOING TO INVITE YOU!!

THAT'S A GOOD IDEA...I THINK YOU'RE DOING THE RIGHT THING...

IF I HAVE THE TYPE OF PERSONALITY THAT ANNOYS YOU, IT WOULD BE SILLY TO INVITE ME..

SCHULZ

ARE YOU GOING TO NURSERY SCHOOL THESE DAYS, LUCY?

YES, I'VE BEEN REINSTATED
IS IT FUN?

IS IT FUN?! ALL WE HAVE TO DO EVERY DAY IS PLAY PLAY PLAY PLAY PLAY PLAY...

I'VE NEVER BEEN SO BORED IN ALL MY LIFE!
SCHULZ

LISTEN!! WHAT'S THAT?
WHAT'S WHAT?

IT'S COMING THIS WAY!
THUMP
THUMP
THUMP
THUMP

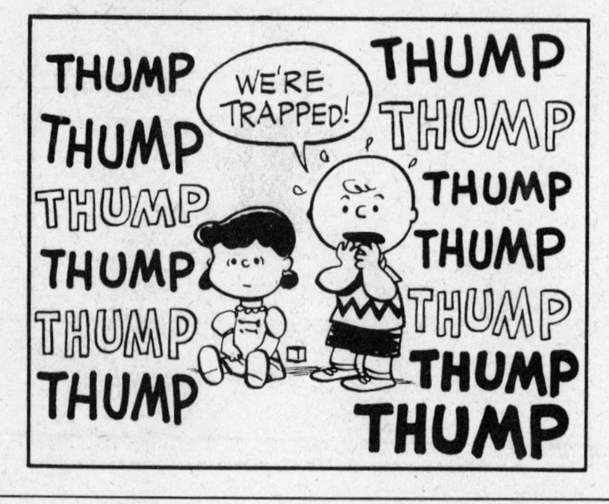
THUMP
THUMP
THUMP
THUMP
THUMP
THUMP
WE'RE TRAPPED!
THUMP
THUMP
THUMP
THUMP
THUMP
THUMP
THUMP

SCHULZ
IT'S LINUS IN HIS NEW SLEEPING BAG..
THUMP THUMP THUMP

WHO TORE MY NEW COMIC MAGAZINE?!

WAS IT YOU, LINUS?! DID YOU TEAR IT?!

NOW, DON'T GO BLAMING LINUS..

HE'S JUST AN INNOCENT BY-SITTER!
SCHULZ

HOW DO YOU LIKE MY NEW DOLL, CHARLIE BROWN?

I'VE NAMED HIM AFTER YOU
REALLY? THAT'S VERY FLATTERING

YES, SIR... THAT'S VERY FLATTERING

TAKE THAT, CHARLIE BROWN!
!
SCHULZ

WHY AREN'T YOU IN SCHOOL?
SCHULZ

SCHULZ
BUMP!
BUMP!!
BUMP!

SCHULZ

THAT'S A NICE MELODY...I WONDER WHAT IT IS...

I THINK IT'S THE 'GLORIA CHORAL'
REALLY? SAY YOU'RE GETTING PRETTY SHARP, CHARLIE BROWN... YES, SIR!

IT'S WRITTEN ON THE SIDE OF THE TOP
SCHULZ

I'VE BEEN PRACTICING TEN HOURS A DAY

I CAN PLAY EVERYTHING BRAHMS OR BEETHOVEN WROTE PLUS AN ABUNDANCE OF BACH & BARTOK

LAST NIGHT ON TELEVISION I SAW A MAN PLAY THE PIANO WITH HIS NOSE...

WHAT'S THE USE?
SCHULZ

HEY! CHARLIE BROWN!

WAIT FOR ME....

WAIT FOR ME...

ALL RIGHT FOR YOU!!
SCHULZ

WHAT ARE YOU EATING?
THIS IS "SPITE" CANDY...

SNOOPY'S ON THE OTHER SIDE OF THIS DOOR...I'M EATING ALL THIS CANDY JUST TO SPITE HIM!

THERE'S ONLY ONE THING WRONG...

"SPITE" CANDY NEVER TASTES VERY GOOD
SCHULZ

QUACK
QUACK
QUACK

WHEN DID YOU GET THE DUCK, LUCY?
I GOT IT FOR MY BIRTHDAY

I'VE NEVER SEEN ANYTHING LIKE IT.. WHEN IT MOVES, THE EYES OPEN AND CLOSE, AND IT SAYS, "QUACK-QUACK"

I FEEL LIKE A **FOOL** PULLING IT AROUND!
SCHULZ

Charlie

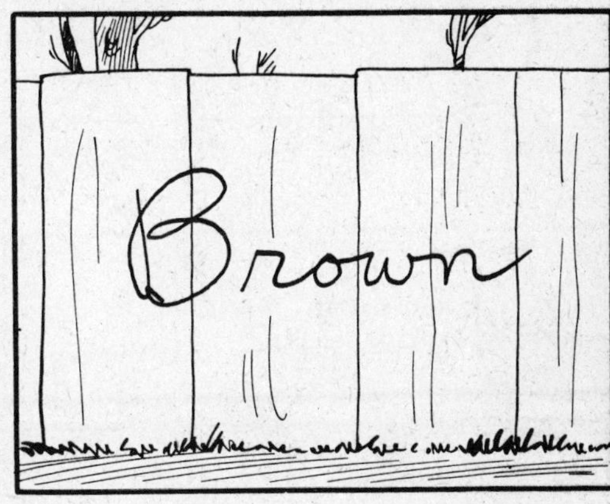
Brown

loves

all
the
girls
SCHULZ

WHEN I GROW UP, I WANT TO BE A NURSE..

THAT'S FINE

WHAT DO YOU WANT TO BE WHEN YOU GROW UP, CHARLIE BROWN?

PERFECT
SCHULZ

AH! THIS IS JUST THE SONG I'VE BEEN WAITING TO HEAR..

HMM...THAT IS NICE...TA DE DA DE DUM TE TA DE DUM... DA DE DUM TE DA DE DUM

DA DE DA DE DA DE DUM DE DA DE DAAA DEE DA DA DE DA

?
SCHULZ

SAY, LINUS... THAT'S SOME CAP!

WHY DON'T YOU TRY WEARING IT MORE TO ONE SIDE?
?

THERE..NOW YOU LOOK REAL JAUNTY!

KLUNK!
SCHULZ

HEY!
HEY!

LOOK HERE...I'D MUCH PREFER HAVING YOU CALL ME BY MY NAME...IT'S ONLY COMMON COURTESY, YOU KNOW...

NO MATTER WHAT YOU MAY THINK OF A FELLOW PERSONALLY, HE STILL DESERVES...
WHERE HAVE YOU BEEN, SNOOPY?

I'VE BEEN CALLING YOU AND CALLING YOU...
SCHULZ

THE ONLY THING THAT INTERESTS HIM IS THE DOG-FOOD COMMERCIALS!
SCHULZ

NOBODY LOVES ME...EVERYBODY HATES ME!
I DIDN'T GET A SINGLE VALENTINE! NOT ONE!!

THAT'S AWFUL, CHARLIE BROWN.. HERE...HOW DO YOU LIKE THIS?
FOR ME? OH, BOY! WOW!

THIS IS SOMETHING! A REAL VALENTINE!
DON'T TAKE IT TOO SERIOUSLY...
SCHULZ

I'M JUST LOANING IT TO YOU SO YOU WON'T FEEL BAD

HOW'S NURSERY SCHOOL, LUCY?

O.K., I GUESS....WE DID FINGER-PAINTINGS TODAY

REALLY? THAT'S FUN, ISN'T IT?
I SUPPOSE SO.. MINE DIDN'T TURN OUT VERY WELL..
SCHULZ

I WAS ALL THUMBS

"GEORGIE PORGY PUDDIN' AN' PIE...

KISSED THE GIRLS, AND MADE THEM CRY...WHEN THE BOYS CAME OUT TO PLAY,..

GEORGIE PORGY RAN AWAY"

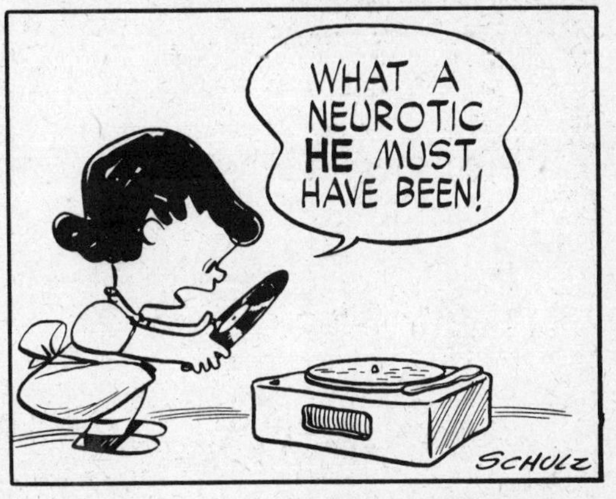
WHAT A NEUROTIC **HE** MUST HAVE BEEN!
SCHULZ

SMACK
?

HEY! STOP THAT!

WAAH!
WHY IS HE CRYING? ALL SNOOPY DID WAS LICK HIS FACE...
SCHULZ

BUT NOW HE WANTS TO GO LICK SNOOPY'S FACE!

SCHULZ

CHARLIE BROWN, WILL YOU MAKE ME A SANDWICH?
WHAT?!

GOOD GRIEF, LUCY!! YOU'RE GOING TO DRIVE ME CRAZY! WHAT A NUISANCE!

DON'T YOU THINK I'VE GOT ANYTHING ELSE TO DO?! WHY DO YOU ALWAYS BOTHER ME?!

ARE YOU THROUGH?
YES, I GUESS SO... *SIGH* WHAT KIND OF SANDWICH DO YOU WANT?
SCHULZ

BOY! WHAT A GAUDY OUTFIT!!

I WOULDN'T BE SEEN AT A DOGFIGHT WITH SUCH AN OUTFIT!

YOU NEVER SHOULD HAVE SAID THAT...

HE WAS ON HIS WAY TO A DOGFIGHT!
SCHULZ

MEN ARE INFINITELY SUPERIOR TO WOMEN!

SIXTY-EIGHT PERCENT OF ALL THE MEN IN THIS COUNTRY ARE COLLEGE GRADUATES! NINETY-THREE PERCENT ARE OVER SIX FEET TALL!

SEVENTY-FOUR PERCENT OF ALL THE MEN IN THE WORLD ARE OF AN EVEN TEMPERAMENT!

WHERE DID YOU GET THOSE FIGURES?
I JUST NOW MADE THEM UP!
SCHULZ

SEE? HE'S BALANCING A BOTTLE OF POP ON HIS EAR..

ISN'T THAT AMAZING?
AMAZING! WHAT FLAVOR IS IT?

GRAPE

OH...WELL! NO WONDER!
SCHULZ

HEY! LOOK AT LINUS!

THIS IS THE FIRST TIME HE'S STOOD BY HIMSELF!
SHOW HIM YOU'RE PROUD OF HIM... GIVE HIM A COOKIE..

HERE, LINUS...

SCHULZ
KLUNK!

OPEN YOUR MOUTH, SNOOPY...

HERE..... CATCH!

NO ... I'VE CHANGED MY MIND...I THINK I'LL EAT THIS MYSELF!

?
SCHULZ

THIS SONG ALWAYS DEPRESSES ME

IT BRINGS BACK SUCH SAD MEMORIES.... YOU KNOW WHAT I MEAN?

I'VE NEVER HEARD ANOTHER SONG THAT DEPRESSES ME THE WAY THIS ONE DOES...

PLAY IT AGAIN, WILL YOU?
SCHULZ

ALL RIGHT! ALL RIGHT!! I'LL LET YOU CARRY MY MAGAZINE
COMIX

ANYTHING TO KEEP PEACE IN THE FAMILY

WE'RE HOME NOW... YOU CAN GIVE IT TO ME...THANK YOU VERY MUCH

SIGH
SCHULZ

EVERYBODY'S BEEN TEASING ME, CHARLIE BROWN..
WHY?

THEY SAY THAT YOU'RE MY BOY FRIEND...ISN'T THAT FUNNY?
OH, YES... THAT'S A RIOT

DO YOU THINK WE'LL EVER GET MARRIED?
NOT UNLESS I LOSE MY MIND!

WELL, AT LEAST THERE'S **SOME** HOPE...
SCHULZ

!
BANG
BANG

LOOK HERE...YOU'RE DOING THAT ALL WRONG..A SPACE-GUN DOESN'T GO, 'BANG'...IT GOES, 'BRZAAAP'

'BRGZAPF'?
NO, 'BRZAAAP'

I WAS BORN IN THE WRONG CENTURY
SCHULZ

WHICH WOULD YOU LIKE, SHERMY, CHOCOLATE OR PEPPERMINT?

TELL HER YOU CAN'T MAKE UP YOUR MIND... THEN SHE'LL GIVE YOU BOTH

I CAN'T MAKE UP MY MIND

ALL RIGHT, THEN I WON'T GIVE YOU EITHER ONE!
SCHULZ

GIMME THAT!

LUCY! YOU DIDN'T TAKE LINUS' COOKIE FROM HIM, DID YOU?

OH, NO, MOTHER...HE OFFERED TO SHARE IT WITH ME..

HO HO!
SCHULZ

PATTY'S WINNING ALL YOUR MARBLES, HUH, CHARLIE BROWN?
PLINK!

YES, BUT I'M A GOOD SPORT ABOUT IT...FAIR PLAY IS MORE IMPORTANT THAN WINNING, YOU KNOW... GOOD SPORTSMANSHIP MUST BE..

ISN'T THAT YOUR FAVORITE "SHOOTER" SHE'S AIMING AT?
!
SCHULZ

LOOK OUT! LOOK OUT!! YOU'RE GONNA MISS! YOU'RE GONNA MISS!!

BEAT AGAIN!! NINE HUNDRED MARBLES! GONE!!
PLINK!

I GET SO MAD I CAN HARDLY SEE!
IT IS DISGUSTING WHEN YOU LOSE ALL THE TIME

IT'S NOT THE PRINCIPLE OF THE THING THAT BOTHERS ME..

I JUST HATE TO LOSE ALL THOSE MARBLES!
SCHULZ

WOULD YOU LIKE TO JOIN OUR CLUB, CHARLIE BROWN ?

WHY, SURE...ABSOLUTELY... I'M VERY FLATTERED THAT YOU SHOULD ASK ME

PSSPSSPSS... PSSP...HUH ?
UH, HUH..
SCHULZ

WE JUST TOOK A VOTE.. YOU'VE BEEN REJECTED!

CIRCUS
5
BIG
DAYS

HAS YOUR MOTHER MENTIONED ANYTHING ABOUT TAKING YOU TO THE CIRCUS, LUCY?

SHE'S DONE A LOT MORE THAN JUST MENTION IT...

SHE'S BEEN HOLDING IT OVER MY HEAD FOR A WEEK!
SCHULZ

"A" IS FOR ALLIGATOR...

AND "B" IS FOR BEAR, AND "C" IS FOR CAT....

AND "D" IS FOR...

DEER!
SCHULZ

YOU'RE DOING GREAT, CHARLIE BROWN...

YOUR SLOW BALL HAS REALLY GOT 'EM GUESSING

WHY DON'T YOU CROSS 'EM UP NOW, AND START THROWING YOUR FAST BALL?

THAT IS MY FAST BALL I'M THROWING!
SCHULZ

YOU DON'T LIKE ME, DO YOU, CHARLIE BROWN?

WELL, YOU DON'T LIKE ME EITHER, SO WE'RE EVEN!

YOU MEAN IF I LIKED YOU, YOU'D LIKE ME?
SURE,...IT'S ONLY NATURAL

MAYBE, BUT IT'S NOT WORTH IT!
SCHULZ

BANG!
!

HEY! I'M ON YOUR SIDE!!

OH ...I'M SORRY, CHARLIE BROWN...

IT'S A GOOD THING I MISSED YOU, ISN'T IT?
SCHULZ

ALL RIGHT, MEN! ON TO MARS!!

THE BOYS CERTAINLY SEEM ENVIOUS OF YOUR NEW SPACE-SUIT, LUCY...

YOU WON'T TELL THEM, WILL YOU?
TELL THEM WHAT?

THESE ARE MY SLEEPERS!
SCHULZ

WHAT'S THE SCORE NOW, SCHROEDER?

EIGHTY-THREE TO SEVENTY-NINE...WE'RE STILL AHEAD
GOOD..

THIS BALL BELONGS TO YOU, DOESN'T IT?

HERE...TAKE IT, AND RUN FOR HOME!!
SCHULZ

?

?

I WON AGAIN! DID YOU MARK IT DOWN?
YES, I MARKED IT DOWN!!! GO AHEAD... START ANOTHER GAME!
SCHULZ

I'M TRYING TO DO A PORTRAIT OF CHARLIE BROWN..

BUT I JUST CAN'T SEEM TO GET THE SHAPE OF HIS HEAD RIGHT...

WHY DON'T YOU USE A COMPASS? OR TRACE AROUND A PIE PLATE?
!

WHEE!
SCHULZ

Adagio sost
sempre pp

LOOK, SCHROEDER...A TOY VIOLIN! DO YOU THINK YOU COULD PLAY A LITTLE BEETHOVEN ON IT?

BEETHOVEN?! ON A TOY VIOLIN?!!

HOW DO YOU EXPECT A PERSON TO PLAY BEETHOVEN ON A TOY VIOLIN?!
SCHULZ

THIS IS MY SANDBOX, SEE?

AND AS LONG AS THIS IS MY SANDBOX, WE'RE GOING TO PLAY WHAT I WANT TO PLAY, SEE?!

THAT'S BECAUSE THIS IS MY SANDBOX, AND AS LONG AS...

SCHULZ
!

WHAT'S GOING ON NOW?

THE OTHER TEAM HAS CALLED 'TIME OUT'

WE MUST REALLY HAVE 'EM WORRIED, HUH?

NO...THAT LAST PITCH OF YOURS FLEW OVER THE BACKSTOP, AND ROLLED DOWN THE SEWER
SCHULZ

SIT UP SNOOPY.. THAT'S THE BOY...

HEY, YOU FORGOT SOMETHING, DIDN'T YOU?
OH! I'M SORRY..

AT EASE!
SCHULZ

THINGS LOOK PRETTY BAD, CHARLIE BROWN...

YOU MEAN THEY'VE CAUGHT ON TO OUR SIGNALS AGAIN?
YUP

THEY KNOW JUST WHAT I'M GOING TO PITCH, HUH?
WORSE THAN THAT...

THEY NO LONGER EVEN **CARE** WHAT YOU'RE GOING TO PITCH!
SCHULZ

IT'S FLYING! LOOK! IT'S FLYING!!
OH, GOOD GRIEF!

THIS MAKES YOU JEALOUS, HUH, CHARLIE BROWN?

JEALOUS, NOTHING!

ANYBODY CAN FLY A **BALLOON**!
SCHULZ

AAK! FOOEY!

WELL, NOBODY **ASKED** YOU TO CHASE A COTTON PRACTICE BALL!!
AAK
SCHULZ

I CAN'T GET ANYONE TO GO TO THE SHOW WITH ME, CHARLIE BROWN..

I'VE ALREADY ASKED PATTY AND SCHROEDER AND LUCY AND SHERMY, BUT NONE OF THEM CAN GO...

AS A LAST RESORT I THOUGHT I'D ASK YOU..
I DON'T MIND PLAYING 'SECOND FIDDLE'...

BUT **I'M** NOT EVEN PART OF THE ORCHESTRA!
SCHULZ

O Freunde, nicht diese Töne! Sondern lasse uns angehnemere..

Freude, schöner Götterfunken, Tochter aus Elysium...

SAY, SCHROEDER, ISN'T TODAY THE DAY YOU PROMISED TO COME OVER, AND PLAY 'THREE BLIND MICE' FOR MY BABY BROTHER ?

ONLY THREE YEARS OLD AND ALREADY I'M FORCED TO GO COMMERCIAL !
SCHULZ

SCHULZ

I GOT IT!!

IT'S ALL MINE!!

PLUNK

ALL RIGHT! YOU'RE SO SMART! LET'S SEE YOU THROW IT BACK!
SCHULZ

WAIT A MINUTE! WHAT'S THIS?!

SNIF SNIF

ALL RIGHT! WHO PUT THE MOTH BALL IN THE RING?!
SCHULZ

MAY I BORROW ONE OF YOUR RECORDS, SCHROEDER?

WHY, SURE, CHARLIE BROWN... I'M GLAD TO SEE YOU'RE TAKING AN INTEREST IN GOOD MUSIC..

HERE....YOU'LL LIKE THIS BEETHOVEN SONATA..THE FIRST MOVEMENT IS REAL NICE, AND..

WE'RE HAVING A BALL GAME, AND WE NEED SOMETHING TO USE FOR HOME PLATE !
SCHULZ

♪

?

!

AAK
SCHULZ

SNOOPY HAD TO MOVE OUT OF HIS HOUSE..

REALLY? WHERE'S HE LIVING NOW?
IN A DUPLEX

A **DUPLEX** ?!
UH, HUH..

SCHULZ

WHAT A BLOCKHEAD THAT CHARLIE BROWN IS!

I WONDER WHO EVER TOLD HIM HE COULD PITCH?! HE GETS WORSE EVERY INNING!

YOU'RE DOING GREAT, OL' PAL!! KEEP UP THE GOOD WORK!

WHAT A BLOCKHEAD THAT CHARLIE BROWN IS!
SCHULZ

NOBODY LOVES ME.. EVERYBODY HATES ME...

SOMETIMES I GET SO DEPRESSED..

BUT ALL IT TAKES TO CHEER ME UP IS A SMILE FROM A DOG...
SCHULZ

HERE.. TAKE A LOOK AT MY FIRST COMIC STRIP

THIS BIRD IS EATING THIS WORM, SEE?...

AND THIS OTHER BIRD SAYS TO HIM, "HOW CAN YOU EAT THAT WORM? IT LOOKS JUST LIKE SPAGHETTI!"

MY HUMOR IS TOO SUBTLE FOR THE AVERAGE READER..
SCHULZ

?

SCHULZ
!

NURSERY SCHOOL WILL BE OVER IN A FEW WEEKS, AND WILL I EVER BE GLAD!

NO MORE HAVING TO PLAY IN THAT OL' SANDBOX AND SWINGING ON THOSE CRAZY SWINGS

JUST THINK... I'LL BE ABLE TO STAY HOME EVERY DAY...

THEN I CAN PLAY IN MY SANDBOX, AND SWING ON MY SWING!
SCHULZ

WHAT IN THE WORLD ARE YOU DOING?

I'M IN BUSINESS...

PUTTING DIRT IN BOXES?
HUH!! THERE'S MORE TO IT THAN THAT..

THESE ARE **READY-MIX** MUD PIES!
SCHULZ

WE'VE BUILT A PITCHER'S MOUND FOR YOU CHARLIE BROWN...
REALLY?

WE THOUGHT IT MIGHT HELP YOUR DELIVERY...
BOY, I'LL SAY IT WILL!

GEE, A REAL MOUND.. THIS WILL IMPROVE MY PITCHING A HUNDRED PERCENT...

I'M AFRAID TO MOVE!
SCHULZ

WHY SHOULD I GO OVER TO YOUR HOUSE?

YOU ALWAYS GET MAD, AND TELL ME TO GO HOME!

WELL, I SUPPOSE WE COULD PLAY AT YOUR HOUSE..

THEN WHEN I GET MAD, YOU'LL ALREADY BE HOME!
SCHULZ

HMM..

ALL RIGHT...WE'LL PLAY IT ONCE MORE, BUT JUST ONCE MORE! THAT'S ALL!

THREE HUNDRED TIMES IS ENOUGH FOR ANYONE TO LISTEN TO "DOGGIE IN THE WINDOW"!
SCHULZ

SOMETIMES I GET SO MAD AT YOU!

YOU...YOU...YOU..YOU OL' CHARLIE BROWN!!!

WHAT AN INSULT!
SCHULZ

DID YOU HEAR ABOUT VIOLET FALLING OFF HER TRICYCLE?
HEAR ABOUT IT?! I WAS THERE!

I TOLD HER SHE WAS GOING TOO FAST! I WARNED HER! I TOLD HER! I TOLD HER AGAIN AND AGAIN!

I KNOW WHAT TRICYCLES CAN DO! I WARNED HER A DOZEN TIMES! I SAID TO HER, 'I KNOW ALL ABOUT TRICYCLES, AND I...

THE WRONG PERSON FELL OFF THAT TRICYCLE!
WHAT? WHAT DO YOU MEAN? HUH? WHO? WHAT? HUH?
SCHULZ

DID YOU GET THE BIRTHDAY CARD I SENT, PATTY?
HUH?.. OH... OH, YES.. I GOT IT..

IT WAS A NICE ONE, WASN'T IT?
HUH?.. OH... OH YES...IT WAS NICE

YOU DIDN'T THANK ME FOR IT...
HUH? OH... OH, DIDN'T I? WELL, THANK YOU..

SCHULZ
I LIKE TO DO THINGS FOR PEOPLE WHO APPRECIATE THEM...

!

SCHULZ

JUST HOLD YOUR CUP UNDER THE FAUCET...
?

ALL YOU HAVE TO DO IS ADD WATER...SEE?
UH, HUH..

IT LOOKS GOOD... WHAT IS IT?

"INSTANT" WATER!
SCHULZ

NOW, LET'S SEE.. WHERE IS THAT CHARLIE BROWN HIDING?

HE'S NOT OVER HERE..

AND HE'S NOT AROUND HERE...

THEN HE MUST NOT BE ANYPLACE!
!
SCHULZ

I'M TIRED OF ALWAYS ASKING THE OTHER KIDS TO PLAY WITH ME!

WHY SHOULD I HAVE TO CALL THEM ALL THE TIME?! LET THEM CALL FOR ME FOR A CHANGE!

I'LL JUST SIT RIGHT HERE...THAT'S WHAT I'LL DO!
I'LL SIT HERE ON MY FRONT STEP, AND LET THEM CALL FOR ME!

WELL.....THAT WAS A DAY WASTED..

IF I WERE THE ONLY GIRL ON EARTH, WOULD YOU LIKE ME, CHARLIE BROWN?

YOU MEAN IF THERE WERE NO DOGS AROUND, EITHER ? OR CATS?

OR IF THERE WERE NO GOLDFISH, OR HORSES, OR LAMBS, OR CHIPMUNKS OR NOTHING?

IN THAT CASE, I MIGHT
SCHULZ

HERE GOES THE LITTLE RACER CAR UP THE HILL...

AND HERE GOES THE LITTLE RACER CAR DOWN THE HILL...

NOW, HERE COMES THE GREAT BIG TRUCK OUT OF CONTROL ABOUT TO SMASH INTO THE HILL...
!
VAN

SCHULZ

YOU GO HOME, CHARLIE BROWN!!
ET
LA
RK

GO ON, I SAID!! GET OUT OF HERE!
ALL RIGHT, I WILL!

HEY! YOU DON'T HAVE TO GO AWAY MAD...
SCHULZ

HEY!
WHAT DO YOU THINK YOU'RE DOING?!!!

I LEFT MY CANDY BAR THERE ON THE SIDEWALK, AND SNOOPY ATE IT!

WELL, WHAT DO YOU EXPECT? HE'S A DOG, ISN'T HE?

DON'T THINK YOU CAN GET AWAY WITH THAT EXCUSE FOREVER!
SCHULZ

NO! I DON'T WANT TO PLAY CHECKERS!

WHAT FUN IS IT FOR ME? I ALWAYS LOSE
BUT THAT'S NOT YOUR FAULT, CHARLIE BROWN..

YOU CAN'T HELP IT IF YOU PLAY STUPIDLY!

I GUESS YOU'RE RIGHT...THAT MAKES ME FEEL BETTER
SCHULZ

YUM YUM

SMACK SMACK

IS IT GOOD?

SCHULZ

YOU'RE THE ONLY FRIEND I'VE GOT, SNOOPY..

YES, SIR, YOU'RE THE ONLY ONE WHO STAYS WITH ME..

YOU'RE THE ONLY ONE WHO WILL FOLLOW ME WHEREVER I GO..

SCHULZ

?

I'M STUDYING BUGS...I'VE BEEN WAITING ALL MORNING FOR THIS ONE TO MOVE..

THAT'S NO BUG! THAT'S JUST A MARK ON THE SIDEWALK!

IT'S A GOOD THING YOU CAME ALONG... I WOULD HAVE STAYED THERE ALL DAY!
SCHULZ

?

?
?

BONK!

!
SCHULZ

?

I WAS LOOKING AT THE CALENDAR, AND I JUST HAPPENED TO NOTICE THAT SOMEBODY HAS PUT A RING AROUND AUGUST FOURTH...

I PUT THAT THERE FOR SNOOPY
YOU'VE HEARD THE OLD SAYING, "EVERY DOG HAS HIS DAY," HAVEN'T YOU?

WELL, AUGUST FOURTH IS SNOOPY'S, AND HE'S NOT TAKING ANY CHANCES ON FORGETTING IT!
SCHULZ

A QUARTER! I FOUND A QUARTER!
I'M RICH!

I CAN BUY CANDY! ICE CREAM! ANYTHING I WANT!

I CAN BUY GUM! I CAN BUY...

SCHULZ

LUCY, WE'RE GOING TO LET YOU PLAY CENTER FIELD..
SWELL!

?

I THOUGHT YOU WERE OUT IN CENTER FIELD?!
I WAS..

BUT I GOT LONESOME..
SCHULZ

IT WAS A REAL GOOD SHOW..
JUST LOOK AT THOSE TWO...

WAS THERE LOTS OF SHOOTING?
I'LL BET THEY'RE TALKING ABOUT ME...

I STAYED TO SEE IT THREE TIMES...
I WONDER WHAT THEY'RE SAYING ABOUT ME?

WERE THERE ANY INDIANS?
IT ALWAYS WORRIES ME WHEN I KNOW THAT PEOPLE ARE TALKING ABOUT ME..
SCHULZ

LAP! LAP! LAP!
LAP! LAP! LAP! LAP!
LAP! LAP!

WE'RE HAVING AN ICE-CREAM-CONE EATING RACE...
LAP! LAP! LAP!

WHO'S AHEAD?
LAP!
LAP!

LUCY...BY TWO LAPS!
SCHULZ

GUESS WHAT I'M WHISTLING, CHARLIE BROWN...

"OLD BLACK JOE"? "TAKE ME OUT TO THE BALL GAME"? "HOME ON THE RANGE"?

NOPE...IT WAS THE LAST HALF OF THE TENTH MEASURE OF SINDING'S OP.32, NO.3

Y'KNOW, I ALMOST SAID THAT...I DON'T KNOW WHY I DIDN'T!
SCHULZ

SHERMY!

TRY IT AGAIN..
SHERMY

I'LL BE RIGHT OUT..

THANKS, LUCY...IF I NEED YOU AGAIN, I'LL LET YOU KNOW..
SCHULZ

CHARLIE BROWN, DO YOU CARE IF I HIT YOU WITH THIS PAPER?

IF YOU KNOW WHAT'S GOOD FOR YOU, YOU'LL GET OUT OF HERE, AND LEAVE ME ALONE..

POW!
SCHULZ

I NEVER KNOW WHAT'S GOOD FOR ME!

GIMME SOME CANDY!
I DON'T THINK IT WOULD BE GOOD FOR YOU, CHARLIE BROWN

I THOUGHT OF OFFERING YOU SOME, BUT I DIDN'T WANT TO SEE YOU GET SICK...
CHOMP CHOMP

THIS IS VERY TOUCHING... SOMEONE IS ACTUALLY LOOKING OUT FOR MY WELFARE...
I KNEW YOU'D SEE IT THAT WAY
SNIF!
CHOMP CHOMP

GIMME SOME CANDY!
SCHULZ

HEY, SNOOPY! WHAT'S YOUR HURRY?

ARF! ARF! ARF! ARF! ARF!!

ARF?
ARF!

SCHULZ

"HUMPTY DUMPTY SAT ON A WALL..HUMPTY DUMPTY HAD A GREAT FALL..

ALL THE KING'S HORSES AND ALL THE KING'S MEN...

COULDN'T PUT HUMPTY DUMPTY TOGETHER AGAIN"

THAT'S THE WAY IT GOES..
SCHULZ

BANG
BANG
BANG

ALL RIGHT.. DROP THAT GUN!

!
SCHULZ

MY DAD BOUGHT ME A NEW GYM SET...

IT'S GOT TWO SWINGS ON IT A PARALLEL BAR, A TEETER-TOTTER, A PAIR OF RINGS AND A TRAPEZE..

ON THE SIDES IT'S GOT A BELL, A WATER SPRAY, A BASKETBALL HOOP, A SIREN, A SLIDE AND A BIG UMBRELLA

I'M SCARED TO GO NEAR THE THING!
SCHULZ

DO YOU STILL GO TO NURSERY SCHOOL EVERY MORNING, LUCY?

NO, THAT'S ALL THROUGH FOR THE SUMMER... NOW I GO TO PICNIC-SCHOOL TWO DAYS A WEEK

MY MOTHER THINKS THIS IS A LOT BETTER..
WHY? DO YOU LEARN MORE?

NO, I'M GONE ALL DAY!
SCHULZ

CHARLIE BROWN WILL BE THE DADDY, I'LL BE THE MOMMY AND YOU'LL BE OUR LITTLE GIRL...

NOW, DON'T BOTHER ME! I'M WASHING DISHES!
AND DON'T BOTHER ME! I'M READING THE PAPER!

I QUIT!!

WHY SHOULD I PLAY SOMETHING I HAVE TO GO THROUGH EVERYDAY?!!
SCHULZ

HEH, HEH, HEH
SCHULZ

I WAS RIGHT! I WAS RIGHT!

SEE? THE DICTIONARY PROVES I WAS RIGHT! HA! WHAT DO YOU THINK OF THAT?!

YOU HAVE A HOMELY FACE!

SCHULZ

SIGH

WHAT'S THE MATTER, CHARLIE BROWN?
I'M A LONESOME COWBOY

WHY ARE YOU SO LONESOME?

ALL THE OTHER KIDS ARE PLAYING "SPACEMAN"
SCHULZ

HEY! DON'T PUT YOUR FINGERS IN THE POPCORN AFTER YOU'VE LICKED THEM!

DO YOU THINK I WANT TO EAT THAT POPCORN AFTER YOU'VE BEEN PUTTING YOUR WET FINGERS IN IT?!

DO YOU THINK I WANT TO EAT WET, STICKY OL' POPCORN THAT YOU'VE TOUCHED WITH YOUR WET, STICKY OL' FINGERS AFTER YOU..

SCHULZ

SPEAK!

ARF!!

WELL, GOOD GRIEF, SNOOPY...YOU DIDN'T HAVE TO..
SCHULZ

SHOUT!

GO ON, SCHROEDER, GET IN...DON'T BE SCARED!

NOW LIE ON YOUR STOMACH, AND MOVE YOUR ARMS LIKE THIS...YOU HAVE TO GET RIGHT DOWN IN THE WATER... DON'T BE A COWARD!

WHY DON'T YOU GET IN AND SHOW HIM HOW?
SCHULZ

NOT ME! I'M SCARED TO DEATH OF WATER!

SLUP-SLUP! LAP-LAP! SLUP!

SLURP-SLURP!

CHOMP, SLUP SLURP
I GUESS I'LL HAVE TO MOVE TO THE COUNTRY...
SCHULZ

I HATE THE SOUNDS OF THE CITY DURING THE SUMMER!

'IT IS A WELL-ESTABLISHED FACT THAT DOGS ACT MERELY BY INSTINCT..'

'THEY ARE NOT ABLE TO REASON AS HUMANS DO..'
!

WHY DO YOU READ THINGS LIKE THAT WHEN SNOOPY'S AROUND?

I CAN'T HELP IT... I JUST LIKE TO RUB IT IN!
SCHULZ

DADDY! I WANNA GET OUT!!

DADDY! I WANNA GET OUT!!

DADDY! I WANNA GET OUT!!

?I AM OUT?!
SCHULZ

marcando
ff
p

SCHROEDER, HOW DO YOU MANAGE TO PLAY ALL THOSE GREAT PIECES ON A TOY PIANO?

YOU GOTTA GET THE BREAKS!
SCHULZ

EVERYONE ON OUR TEAM HAS A SPONSOR NOW...

THAT'S VERY NICE, CHARLIE BROWN..
FAMILY BARBER SHOP

HOW ABOUT YOU, SCHROEDER? WHO'S YOUR SPONSOR?

I MIGHT HAVE KNOWN!
BEETH-OVEN
SCHULZ

BOY, ARE YOU EVER A FLOP!! YOU CAN'T DO ANYTHING!

YOU CAN'T EVEN RUN FAST! AND YOU'RE A TERRIBLE BASEBALL PLAYER! YOU'RE NOT GOOD AT ANYTHING! YOU'RE A FLOP!!

MY MOTHER LIKES ME..
SCHULZ

HELLO, SNOOPY? CAN YOU COME OVER RIGHT AWAY?
?

DID I JUST HEAR YOU CALL UP A DOG? AND ON A TOY TELEPHONE?

THAT'S THE MOST RIDICULOUS THING I'VE EVER HEARD!

GLAD TO SEE YOU, SNOOPY... I KNEW YOU'D COME IF I ASKED YOU....
SCHULZ

WHAT ARE YOU GOING TO BE WHEN YOU GROW UP, LUCY?

GROW UP? WHAT DO YOU MEAN?
WHEN YOU GET BIG... YOU KNOW.. TALL.. MATURE.. A LADY...

WELL, I'LL BE...THAT'S A GOOD ONE!

I NEVER KNEW I WAS GOING TO GET ANY BIGGER!
SCHULZ

The boy sees the slide...

The boy wants to go down the slide...

The boy is afraid to go down the slide...

THE BOY IS A HOPELESS CASE...
SCHULZ

BOY, I'M GLAD THAT'S OVER!

I DIDN'T THINK WE'D EVER GET 'EM OUT...

SIXTY-THREE RUNS IN THE VERY FIRST INNING!

THERE GOES OUR SHUTOUT!
SCHULZ

CHASE IT, SNOOPY! BRING IT BACK!

HEY! THIS WAY! IT WENT THIS WAY!!

COME BACK HERE!!
IT'S NO USE..

WHEN FOUR-THIRTY ROLLS AROUND, SNOOPY QUITS FOR THE DAY!
SCHULZ

HOW ABOUT A GAME OF MARBLES, CHARLIE BROWN?

THAT WOULD BE FINE...IF I COULD WIN....BUT I'D PROBABLY LOSE.... THEN I'D GET DEPRESSED...

THEN I'D BE REAL GRUMPY, AND WOULDN'T TALK TO ANYONE, AND I'D HATE MYSELF...
SCHULZ

THANKS, ANYWAY

SCHULZ
B-R-R-R-R

I'M DEPRESSED BECAUSE I FEEL YOU DON'T LOVE ME ANY MORE

I NEVER DID LOVE YOU, CHARLIE BROWN...

REALLY?

THAT MAKES ME FEEL A LOT BETTER!
SCHULZ

HEY, PATTY!

HOW ABOUT GIVING ME A PUSH?

BONK!

THAT WAS A STRANGE THING TO ASK FOR.. ??
SCHULZ

BOY! I THINK I'M LOSING MY MIND

I PUT ON A SLIP OF PAPER ALL THE THINGS I WANTED TO BUY AT THE STORE, SEE?

I'LL BET I KNOW WHAT HAPPENED...YOU FORGOT THE SLIP OF PAPER!
WORSE THAN THAT..

I FORGOT TO GO TO THE STORE!
SCHULZ

YOU'RE CRAZY, CHARLIE BROWN!
YES! YOU'RE CRAZY, CHARLIE BROWN!

AND YOU TALK TOO MUCH!
YES! YOU TALK TOO MUCH!

AND YOU'VE GOT A FUNNY FACE!
SAY! YOU AN' I HAVE A LOT IN COMMON, DON'T WE?

WE BOTH DISLIKE THE SAME THINGS ABOUT CHARLIE BROWN!
SIGH
SCHULZ

..NINE, TEN, ELEVEN, TWELVE..

TWENTY-THREE, TWENTY-FOUR, TWENTY-FIVE

HERE I COME..READY OR NOT...

PEEKED ?! ME?
SCHULZ

THIS IS HOPELESS!

THIS IS LIKE LOOKING FOR A LOST BALL IN THE HIGH WEEDS!

WHAT ARE YOU LOOKING FOR?

A LOST BALL IN THE HIGH WEEDS!
SCHULZ

!

HEY PATTY...
COME QUICK..

HE'S BEEN SITTING
THERE ALL MORNING..

SCHULZ
HE THINKS HE'S
ON TELEVISION!

HOW'S PICNIC
SCHOOL COMING,
LUCY?

NOT SO GOOD... I DO ALL
RIGHT IN LUNCH EATING AND
TEETER TOTTERING...

BUT I'M A COMPLETE
FLOP IN NAP TAKING..

AS LONG AS I'VE GOT
INSOMNIA, I'LL NEVER
GRADUATE!
SCHULZ

BEDTIME!
SCHULZ

WE'LL PRETEND THE INDIANS ARE COMING, SEE?

WE'LL PRETEND THAT THEY CAPTURE YOU, AND THAT THEY TIE YOU TO A STAKE...

AND THEN WE'LL PRETEND THAT..
HOLD IT! I DON'T THINK I'LL PLAY..

I CAN GET A BETTER ROLE IN THE PIRATES GAME GOING ON ACROSS THE STREET..
SCHULZ

C'MON OUT AN' PLAY...

SAY, "PLEASE"

PLEASE!

I CAN'T...MY MOTHER SAYS I HAVE TO STAY IN...
SCHULZ

Z

YOU'RE THE ONLY PERSON I KNOW WHO CAN HEAR SOMEONE EATING MARSHMALLOWS!
SCHULZ

GEE, I'M GLAD IT'S RAINING TODAY...

NOW I CAN STAY INSIDE AND READ

COULDN'T YOU STAY INSIDE AND READ EVEN IF IT WASN'T RAINING?
NO...

WHENEVER THE SUN IS SHINING, I FEEL OBLIGATED TO PLAY OUTSIDE!
SCHULZ

I CAN HARDLY WAIT TO SHOW SOMEONE MY NEW RECORD, "THREE BLIND MICE"
KIDDIE REKORDS

LOOK, VIOLET, MY DAD JUST BOUGHT ME BEETHOVEN'S QUARTET NO. 4!
KIDDIE REKORDS

SAY, WHAT'S IN **THAT** PACKAGE?
KIDDIE REKORDS

THIS? OH,....NOTHING.... NOTHING AT ALL...
SCHULZ

PATTY, DO YOU LIKE ME?
OF COURSE, I LIKE YOU, CHARLIE BROWN..

WHY DO YOU LIKE ME?
OH, I DON'T KNOW... BECAUSE YOU LIKE ME, I SUPPOSE..

THAT'S A PRETTY FLIMSY REASON!
SCHULZ

IS PICNIC SCHOOL OVER FOR THE SUMMER, LUCY?

UH, HUH... I'VE ALREADY STARTED IN AT NURSERY SCHOOL AGAIN..

SIGH

BACK TO THE OLD GRIND!
SCHULZ

COME BACK HERE WITH THAT BALL!

YIPE!

SCHULZ

HERE..YOU CAN HAVE THESE COCONUT ONES.. I DON'T LIKE COCONUT

AND YOU MIGHT JUST AS WELL HAVE THESE GREEN THINGS...I DON'T LIKE THEM EITHER...AND, HERE..TAKE THESE WITH DARK CHOCOLATE..

I CAN'T STAND DARK CHOCOLATE.. AND HERE'S A COUPLE WITH SOME FUNNY STUFF ON TOP...YOU MIGHT AS WELL HAVE THOSE, TOO..

HOW CAN YOU STAND BEING SO GOOD TO ME?
SCHULZ

I WISH I COULD BE MORE LIKE YOU, CHARLIE BROWN..

YOU'RE SO... YOU'RE SO... HOW SHOULD I SAY IT? YOU'RE SO..

PERFECT?

SCHULZ

SCHROEDER DOESN'T PLAY FAIR!

I SHOT HIM, BUT HE WON'T FALL DEAD!
WHERE DID YOU SHOOT HIM?

I SHOT HIM RIGHT BEHIND THE DAVENPORT..

AND IF THAT ISN'T FATAL, I DON'T KNOW WHAT IS!
SCHULZ

WELL! YOU TWO LOOK LIKE YOU'RE HAVING A GOOD TIME..

WE ARE... WE'RE MAKING FUN OF THIS PICTURE IN THE PAPER..

WHY ARE YOU MAKING FUN OF IT?

BECAUSE WE DON'T UNDERSTAND IT..
SCHULZ

SLAM!

RING!
RING!!
SCHULZ

WELL! IF IT ISN'T CHARLIE BROWN!!

JUST LOOK AT ALL THE STARS..

DID YOU EVER SEE SO MANY? THEY'RE ALL OVER.. THE SKY IS COVERED WITH STARS...

STARS, STARS, STARS.. AS FAR AS YOU CAN SEE... I WONDER HOW MANY THERE ARE?

TEN?
SCHULZ

WE NEED A FOURTH FOR BRIDGE, CHARLIE BROWN...

WE HADN'T INTENDED TO ASK YOU, BUT WE COULDN'T FIND ANYONE ELSE...

AFTER LOOKING ALL OVER, WE FINALLY DECIDED ON YOU AS A LAST RESORT!

THERE'S NOTHING LIKE THE FEELING THAT YOU'RE REALLY WANTED!
SCHULZ

HMMMM

HEY, CHARLIE BROWN! I'VE GOT "PERFECT PITCH"!!

YOU MEAN "A PERFECT PITCH"... BESIDES, WHO CARES? THE BASEBALL SEASON IS OVER!

SCHULZ
SOMETIMES I THINK I SHOULD PUT IN FOR A TRANSFER TO A NEW COMIC STRIP!

LET'S SEE NOW...HMM..

NOTHING HERE..NOPE.. NOTHING HERE EITHER

I'M SORRY, CHARLIE BROWN..

I GUESS NOTHING HAS BEEN WRITTEN FOR PIANO AND CIGAR-BOX BANJO..
SCHULZ

SIGNALS! ONE! SIX! THREE! TWO! FIVE! HIKE!

TIME OUT!
?

SAY, CHARLIE BROWN... ABOUT THE WAY YOU CALL THOSE SIGNALS..

I THINK YOU SHOULD TRY MIXING UP THE NUMBERS INSTEAD OF SAYING THEM IN THEIR RIGHT ORDER!
SCHULZ

BOY, AM I EVER DEPRESSED

?

SOMEBODY ELSE IS DEPRESSED TOO, I SEE

THAT'S THE ONLY THING THAT COULD POSSIBLY HAVE CHEERED ME UP!
SCHULZ

SCHULZ

I'M THROUGH BEING PUSHED AROUND! DO YOU HEAR ME ?!

I'M SICK AND TIRED OF ALWAYS BEING THE BASSOON!

THE WORD IS "BUFFOON"!

BEAT AGAIN!
SCHULZ

WHY SHOULD I GO TO SCHOOL?! I'M GOING TO BE A BALLPLAYER WHEN I GROW UP!

BALLPLAYERS ONLY HAVE TO BE ABLE TO COUNT BALLS AND STRIKES!
OH, YEAH? THINK AGAIN, CHARLIE BROWN..

YOU WON'T EVEN BE ABLE TO TELL IF YOU'VE GOT ENOUGH PLAYERS ON THE FIELD...YOU WON'T BE ABLE TO COUNT THAT HIGH!
!

YOU'RE RIGHT...I'D BETTER GO UNTIL I LEARN TO COUNT TO NINE..
SCHULZ

RATS!

IT'S NO USE... I GIVE UP!

WELL, DON'T FEEL SO BADLY ABOUT IT, CHARLIE BROWN.... AFTER ALL..

..MOST COLLEGE PLAYERS ARE BIGGER THAN US!
SCHULZ

BOY, I JUST SAW THE BEST COWBOY SHOW, CHARLIE BROWN

IT WAS ALL ABOUT THIS GUY WHO...
I HAVEN'T SEEN A COWBOY SHOW FOR SOME TIME...

THE LAST ONE I SAW WAS ABOUT THREE WEEKS AGO...IT WAS PRETTY GOOD, TOO...I REMEMBER ONE SCENE WHERE..

SCHULZ
?

DO YOU KNOW WHAT DAY THIS IS, SCHROEDER?

THIS IS 'COLUMBUS DAY'!

OH?

SCHULZ
WHAT DID **HE** COMPOSE?

GO AHEAD! MAKE FUN OF ME! YOU JUST WAIT..

SOMEDAY I'LL GET TO BE PRESIDENT, AND THEN YOU'LL ALL BE SORRY!

I'LL SAY WE WILL..

SOMEHOW THAT DIDN'T COME OUT RIGHT..
SCHULZ

AHEM PARDON ME...

AHEM PARDON ME! *AHEM!* *AHEM!*

GET AWAY FROM MY PIANO!

SCHULZ
SIGH

AND THERE GOES CHARLIE BROWN THRU RIGHT GUARD!

HE SHAKES OFF ONE TACKLER.. AND ANOTHER.. TEARING.. TWISTING.. TURNING..

AND NOW HE'S IN THE CLEAR! HE'S..HE'S... HE'S....

SCHULZ

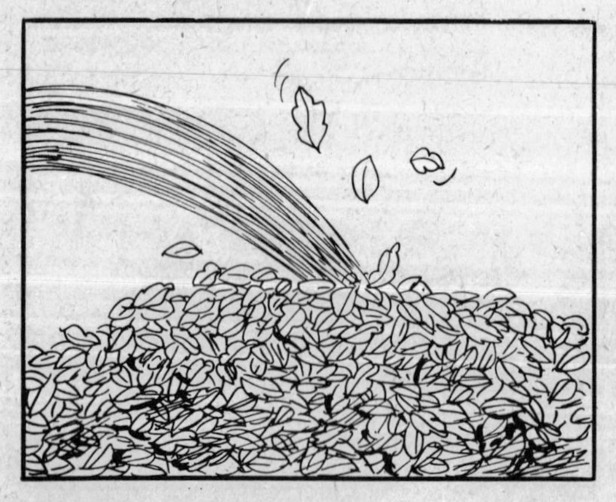

SCHULZ

WHO SHALL WE INVITE TO OUR PARTY?

LET'S NOT INVITE CHARLIE BROWN..
O.K., WE WON'T INVITE CHARLIE BROWN

AND LET'S NOT INVITE LUCY...
FINE...WE WON'T INVITE LUCY

IT'S A LOT MORE FUN NOT INVITING PEOPLE THAN IT IS INVITING THEM!
SCHULZ

LOOK AT THAT, WILL YOU?!

?
JUST LOOK AT THAT!

I DON'T KNOW WHAT'S GOING TO BECOME OF THAT DOG...

HE'S SITTING THERE TRYING TO MAKE PEOPLE THINK THE WIND IS BLOWING!
SCHULZ

DO YOU WANNA HEAR A SECRET, SNOOPY?
?

PSS SSSPP SSS PSSP SSSP

WELL!

AFTER ALL, CHARLIE BROWN...
SCHULZ

poco rit.
ff

I WAS JUST NOTICING SOMETHING, SCHROEDER...AREN'T THE BLACK KEYS ON YOUR PIANO JUST PAINTED ON?
YES,.. I GUESS SO...

WELL, MAYBE THIS IS A FOOLISH QUESTION, BUT IF THOSE KEYS ARE JUST PAINTED ON, HOW DO YOU PLAY ALL THOSE DIFFICULT PIECES?

I PRACTICE A LOT!
SCHULZ

AH?
AH?
AH?

AHCHOO!

SCHULZ

LUCY IS IN CHARGE OF OUR ARTILLERY

THAT'S A BIG JOB FOR SUCH A LITTLE GIRL, ISN'T IT?

BANG

OH, NO... I THINK SHE'S QUITE SUITED FOR THE JOB
SCHULZ

YOU'LL NEVER SCARE ANYBODY WITH THAT PUMPKIN..

HERE.... CATCH!!

NO!NO! DON'T THROW IT! DON'T!DON'T!

SCARED YOU, DIDN'T I?
SCHULZ

"TRICKS OR TREATS, MONEY OR EATS!"

GO AHEAD! DO YOUR WORST! WE DON'T CARE!

SIGH
SCHULZ

HMMM...

LET'S SEE...THE KING FELL ON THAT TRICK AND SO DID THE TEN OF DIAMONDS... HMM...UH, HUH...

I HOPE YOU DON'T MIND MY WRITING ALL THIS DOWN..

IT'S THE ONLY WAY I CAN KEEP TRACK OF WHAT'S BEEN PLAYED!
SCHULZ

BOO!

SCHULZ
BOO!

BOO!
BOO!

KLUNK!

RATS
I GIVE UP!

YOU JUST CAN'T BE A GHOST IN A CONTOUR SHEET!
SCHULZ

BOO!

OH, TAKE THAT SHEET OFF, CHARLIE BROWN...
BOO!

HALLOWEEN WAS YESTERDAY
BOO

OUR LAUNDRY DIDN'T COME BACK UNTIL TODAY
SCHULZ

BUMP
BUMP
BUMP

SPLASH

ISN'T THAT A BRAND-NEW DOLL, LUCY?
UH HUH...

I'M JUST BREAKING IT IN...
SCHULZ

SCHULZ

I DON'T WANNA TAKE A NAP!

YOUR MOTHER KNOWS BEST, LUCY.. GO AHEAD...
NO! I DON'T WANNA TAKE A NAP!!

DON'T BE THAT WAY! NAPS NEVER HURT ANYBODY!
MINE DO!

I ALWAYS FALL OUT OF BED!
SCHULZ

WE THINK YOU'RE WONDERFUL, CHARLIE BROWN!

I'LL BET THAT'S NOT WHAT YOU SAY WHEN MY BACK IS TURNED!
SURE, IT IS... YOU JUST TURN AROUND, AND LISTEN...

THAT CHARLIE BROWN CERTAINLY IS A FINE FELLOW...
I'LL SAY HE IS...GOOD OL' CHARLIE BROWN!

I TAKE IT ALL BACK...YOU GIRLS MUST BE SINCERE!
SCHULZ

SCHULZ

ALL RIGHT.. PUT 'EM UP!

MY MOTHER THINKS I'M WONDERFUL!

I IMAGINE SHE DOES, LUCY...
SHE THINKS I'LL BE A CINCH TO WIN THE TITLE...

WHAT TITLE?
"MISS FUSS-BUDGET OF 1952"

YOUR MOTHER IS A SHREWD JUDGE OF CHARACTER, LUCY
SHE THINKS I'M WONDERFUL
SCHULZ

SNOOPY
SCHULZ

I'M THROUGH WITH SCHOOL! I QUIT!
QUIT?! HA! YOU MUST BE CRAZY, CHARLIE BROWN!

YOU CAN'T QUIT SCHOOL! THEY WON'T LET YOU! YOU'VE GOT TO GO FOR TWELVE MORE YEARS!

DID YOU HEAR ME? TWELVE MORE YEARS! TWELVE LONG YEARS! EVERY DAY! YEAR IN AND YEAR OUT! TWELVE YEARS! TWELVE..

YAAH!
SCHULZ

DO YOU WANNA HEAR A SECRET?
SURE

PROMISE YOU WON'T TELL ANYONE?
I PROMISE

PSST... PSSSST.... PSSPSSPSP...

HEY, VIOLET! YOU SHOULD HEAR WHAT CHARLIE BROWN JUST TOLD ME!
SCHULZ

WAAH!
WHAT'S THE MATTER, LUCY?

HUH?
WHY ARE YOU CRYING?

I'M GLAD YOU ASKED ME THAT.. SIT DOWN RIGHT THERE, AND I'LL EXPLAIN IN DETAIL..

IT ALL STARTED SEVERAL MONTHS AGO... I WAS ON MY WAY TO PATTY'S HOUSE, AND..
SCHULZ

I WON AGAIN! I WON AGAIN!

THAT LAST STUPID PLAY OF YOURS MADE IT A CINCH, CHARLIE BROWN!

JUST THINK,.. I WON AGAIN! I WON AGAIN!
SIGH

AREN'T YOU HAPPY FOR ME?
SCHULZ

YOU KNOW WHAT WE OUGHT TO DO, CHARLIE BROWN?
WHAT?

LET'S GET SNOOPY TO PULL US IN THE WAGON..
SAY! THAT'S A SWELL IDEA!

I CAN SEE US NOW.. TEARING AROUND THE BLOCK.. ZOOM!
WE'LL GO AROUND AND AROUND AND AROUND..
SCHULZ

ON SECOND THOUGHT MAYBE IT WOULDN'T BE MUCH FUN..
YOU'RE RIGHT... LET'S DO SOMETHING ELSE..
WHEW

LOOK AT CHARLIE BROWN PULLING SCHROEDER AROUND...THAT LOOKS LIKE FUN!

HEY, SCHROEDER! ARE YOU ENJOYING YOUR RIDE?!
SCHULZ

I'D ENJOY IT A LOT MORE IF WE HAD A SLED!

LUCY, YOUR MOTHER SAYS YOU'RE A NATURAL-BORN FUSS-BUDGET..

'NATURAL-BORN' NOTHING!

SHE DOESN'T GIVE ME ANY CREDIT...

I'VE WORKED HARD TO BE WHAT I AM!!
SCHULZ

DID I WIN ?!

I DID, DIDN'T I ?!...I FINALLY WON A GAME! I CAN'T BELIEVE IT!

I'VE NEVER BEEN SO HAPPY IN ALL MY LIFE!!!
I JUST LET YOU WIN BECAUSE I FELT SORRY FOR YOU!

IT'S ALWAYS BETTER TO KNOW THE TRUTH
SCHULZ

!
SLURP SLURP SLUP

FOOD!
SLUP SLURP

SLURP SLURP
SCHULZ

CHOMP CHOMP
-GULP-

SORRY, SNOOPY.. THAT WAS THE LAST PIECE..
!

CLUMP!!

DON'T YOU 'CLUMP' THE FLOOR AT ME!
SCHULZ

YOU CERTAINLY HAVE A LOT OF TOYS, LUCY

I GOT ALL OF THESE FOR MY BIRTHDAY... THOSE OVER THERE I GOT FOR HAVING THE MEASLES..

MOST OF THE OTHERS I'VE JUST ACCUMULATED FROM DAY TO DAY...
WHAT ARE YOU GOING TO DO WITH THEM ALL?

I DON'T KNOW... IT'S GETTING SO THEY'RE BUYING THEM FASTER THAN I CAN BREAK THEM!
SCHULZ

ISN'T YOUR FAVORITE RADIO PROGRAM ON AT SIX O'CLOCK?

YOU'RE RIGHT! IT IS!!

HEY! IT'S SIX-THIRTY ALREADY! I'VE MISSED IT!

I KNOW IT... I CAN'T STAND THAT PROGRAM!
SCHULZ

HERE, SNOOPY, CATCH THE BALL...

WELL, NOW... WHAT'S THE MATTER WITH YOU?

TODAY IS SATURDAY...

HE FEELS IT'S HIS DAY OFF
SCHULZ

WAAH!
I HURT MY HAND!

HERE, LUCY...I'LL KISS IT...THAT'LL MAKE IT BETTER..
SMACK

?

OF WHAT MEDICAL VALUE WAS THAT?!
SCHULZ

HEY, SNOOPY..
ZZZ

C'MON..WAKE UP... IT'S TIME TO GO TO BED...

ZZZ
SCHULZ

WHAT HAVE YOU GOT, CHARLIE BROWN?

CANDY BARS... I'VE GOT TWO... WOULD YOU LIKE TO HAVE ONE?

ONE ISN'T ENOUGH... I WANT BOTH OF THEM!

SCHULZ
I ADMIRE FRANKNESS IN A PERSON..

DID YOU GET SOME NICE THINGS FOR YOUR BIRTHDAY, PATTY?
OH, YES... I GOT A SET OF TOY DISHES THAT HAS FIFTY PIECES...

AND I GOT A SET OF BLOCKS WITH A HUNDRED AND NINETY PIECES...

AND I GOT A SEWING-KIT THAT HAS SEVENTY-FIVE PIECES AND A PUZZLE THAT HAS FORTY-EIGHT PIECES...

MY MOTHER SAYS THAT WILL GIVE HER THREE HUNDRED AND SIXTY-THREE MORE THINGS TO PICK UP AROUND THE HOUSE!
SCHULZ

THIS IS A GREAT SCRAPBOOK, SCHROEDER...

I DON'T SEE HOW YOU DID IT...IT'S REALLY AMAZING

I NEVER WOULD HAVE THOUGHT IT WAS POSSIBLE...

AN ENTIRE SCRAPBOOK WITH NOTHING IN IT EXCEPT PICTURES OF BEETHOVEN!
SCHULZ

CHARLIE BROWN IS AN EASY GOING SORT OF FELLOW, ISN'T HE ?
?

I'LL SAY HE IS... GOOD OL' CHARLIE BROWN...
HE SEEMS TO GET ALONG WITH EVERYBODY

NOBODY HATES HIM...
EVERYBODY LIKES HIM...

WHAT A WISHY-WASHY CHARACTER!
SCHULZ

HEY!! LET'S GO!

SAY, ISN'T LINUS COMING OUTSIDE?
NO, IT'S TOO COLD FOR HIM TODAY...

HE'S GOING TO WATCH US THROUGH THE FRONT DOOR..

WHAT WAS THAT YOU JUST GAVE TO SNOOPY?

A MITTEN..
A MITTEN?! YOU GAVE HIM ONE OF YOUR MITTENS TO PLAY WITH?

NO NOT TO PLAY WITH...
TO WEAR!

SCHULZ

I WISH I HAD WORN MY HAT...

MY EARS ARE FREEZING!

THERE'S THE GUY WITH SOMETHING YOU SHOULD HAVE..

'BUILT-IN' EAR MUFFS
SCHULZ

!

SCHULZ

I'LL BET YOU A MILLION DOLLARS THAT I'M RIGHT!

I'LL BET YOU A MILLION BILLION DOLLARS!

I'LL BET YOU A MILLION BILLION TRILLION DOLLARS!!

YOU KNOW I HAVEN'T GOT THAT KIND OF MONEY...
SCHULZ

I'VE BEEN WORKING ON THIS PUZZLE FOR A WEEK!

SHALL I GIVE IT A KICK, AND SCATTER THE PIECES ALL OVER THE ROOM?

NO, I DON'T THINK YOU'D BETTER...

THAT'S WHAT I ALWAYS DO WHEN SOMETHING GETS THE BEST OF ME...

I'M SO PROUD OF MYSELF..

I HAVEN'T DONE ONE MEAN THING TO MY BABY BROTHER TODAY... NOT ONE!

WELL, THAT'S FINE, LUCY...THAT'S REAL FINE...
THERE'S ONLY ONE THING THAT WORRIES ME..

THE DAY ISN'T OVER YET!
SCHULZ

YOU MEAN SANTA COMES DOWN THIS CHIMNEY?
UH HUH

AND THEN CRAWLS OUT OF THIS FIREPLACE?
UH HUH

AND HE DOES THAT IN EVERY HOUSE IN TOWN?
ALL OVER THE WORLD!

WHAT A WAY TO MAKE A LIVING!
SCHULZ

GET OUT OF HERE!

GO ON HOME, CHARLIE BROWN! I DON'T EVER WANT TO SEE YOU AGAIN! NOT EVER!
SIGH

DO YOU HEAR ME ?! NOT EVER, EVER, EVER!!!

I CAN ALWAYS TELL WHEN I'M NOT WANTED...
SCHULZ

WHAT'S GOING ON HERE ?
I'M HELPING SNOOPY TO BURY A BONE..

GOOD GRIEF! CAN'T HE DO THAT HIMSELF ?

HE HATES TO GET HIS HANDS DIRTY!
SCHULZ

YOU KNOW WHAT?
WHAT?

MY GRANDFATHER SAYS WHEN HE WENT TO SCHOOL, HE USED TO DUNK THE GIRLS' PIGTAILS IN THE INKWELL..

IF YOU TRY THAT, I'LL KNOCK YOU CLEAR ACROSS TH' ROOM

THAT'S WHAT HAPPENED TO MY GRANDFATHER..
SCHULZ

THAT WAS AWFUL!

THAT WAS THE WORST PIANO PLAYING I'VE EVER HEARD!!

YOU HAVE ABSOLUTELY NO TALENT WHATSOEVER!

I'M HELPING SCHROEDER TO GET USED TO CRITICISM...
SCHULZ

GUESS WHAT I'M PLAYING, CHARLIE BROWN...

TSCHAIKOWSKI'S MELODY IN E FLAT? SCHUMANN'S TRÄUMEREI? BACH'S FIRST PRELUDE AND FUGUE?

BEETHOVEN'S PROMETHEUS VARIATIONS? CHOPIN'S WALTZ IN C SHARP MINOR?

NOPE...JINGLE BELLS!
SCHULZ

I DID IT!! WHAT A TRIUMPH!

I'M THE FIRST PERSON IN HISTORY WHO'S EVER WON TEN THOUSAND CHECKER GAMES IN A ROW!

HUH! YOU THINK YOU'RE SO SMART! WELL, JUST REMEMBER ONE THING...

I'M THE FIRST PERSON IN HISTORY WHO'S EVER LOST TEN THOUSAND CHECKER GAMES IN A ROW!
SCHULZ

ZZZ

ZZ

CHOMP CHOMP
!

SCHULZ

"'TWAS THE NIGHT BEFORE CHRISTMAS...

AND ALL THROUGH THE HOUSE NOT A CREATURE WAS STIRRING, NOT EVEN A MOUSE..."

BEFORE I CONTINUE, HERE IS A BRIEF WORD FROM THE SPONSOR...

WOULD YOU LIKE TO BUY A MAGAZINE?
10¢
SCHULZ

I'M ADDRESSING ALL MY NEW YEAR'S CARDS, SNOOPY..

WHY DON'T YOU GO OVER, AND GUARD THE DOOR-WAY SO NOBODY COMES IN?

SCHULZ

OUR TELEVISION SCREEN IS BIGGER THAN YOURS!
IT IS? THAT'S FINE. I'LL BET YOU ENJOY IT..

MY DAD MAKES MORE MONEY THAN YOUR DAD...OUR HOUSE IS A LOT BETTER THAN YOURS, TOO!
TIP TOP

I REALIZE THAT...AND I'M VERY HAPPY FOR YOU..

YOU DRIVE ME CRAZY!
SCHULZ

VERY IMAGINATIVE..
THANK YOU

IF YOU'LL STEP OVER HERE, I'LL SHOW YOU ANOTHER ONE OF MY MANY CREATIONS..

THAT IS A SNOWMAN?!
SURE..

HE'S STANDING IN A HOLE!
SCHULZ

HEY, PATTY! GUESS WHAT I GOT FOR CHRISTMAS!

HEY, CHARLIE BROWN! GUESS WHAT I GOT FOR CHRISTMAS!

AN' I GOT A SLED AN' A DOLL! BOY! PUZZLE! AND...CRAYONS!. THAT...AN' LOTS OF... OH, AND WITH..SKATES..AN' CANDY..

WHAT DID YOU SAY?
SCHULZ

I'LL NEVER BE ABLE TO GET TO VIOLET'S PARTY ON TIME..

MAYBE I'D BETTER PHONE, AND TELL HER I'LL BE LATE...

OH, AREN'T YOU HERE YET, CHARLIE BROWN? WE HADN'T EVEN NOTICED!
SCHULZ

THAT'S THE WAY IT GOES...

A
HK
S

Z
HK
S

Z
HK

SCHULZ
Z
S
H
H

KRINKLE

SCHULZ
!

KNOCK KNOCK..
WHO'S THERE?

FUZZ!

HUH?

FUZZ! THERE'S A PIECE OF FUZZ ON THE SIDEWALK!

OH, GOOD GRIEF..
I'M SCARED OF FUZZ! BRUSH IT AWAY, CHARLIE BROWN! BRUSH IT AWAY!

THAT'S THE SILLIEST THING I'VE EVER HEARD! FUZZ!!! GOOD GRIEF!
BRUSH IT AWAY! BRUSH IT AWAY!!

AAK!!
IT MOVED

IT'S A BUG! IT'S A BUG!
IT'S A PIECE OF FUZZ!

LET'S GO BACK THE WAY WE CAME..
WE CAN WALK CLEAR AROUND THE BLOCK SOMEDAY WHEN WE'RE OLDER
FUZZ! BRRR..
SCHULZ

!

SCHULZ
?

I'M DISCOURAGED TODAY, AND WHEN I GET DISCOURAGED, A COMIC MAGAZINE IS THE ONLY THING THAT WILL REVIVE ME

For the Kiddies
WHAT A BEAUTIFUL GORY LAYOUT!

For the Kiddies
THIS DRUGGIST IS AWFULLY FUSSY...HE WON'T LET YOU LOOK AT THE COMIC MAGAZINES UNLESS YOU BUY ONE...
TERROR COMICS
GEE, THE COVER CAME OFF THIS ONE... I HARDLY JERKED IT!
15¢

For the Kiddies
THOSE ON THE TOP ROW LOOK PRETTY GOOD...

WHOOPS!
GASP COMICS
TERROR FUNNIES

HE SHOULD SELL THESE FOR HALF PRICE... WHO WANTS A MAGAZINE AFTER IT'S BEEN LAYING AROUND ON THE FLOOR?

I GUESS I'LL TAKE THIS ONE...

BOY, DID HE EVER GLARE AT ME! HE PROBABLY ISN'T FEELING WELL...
SCHULZ

OH, YOU'RE A BEAUTIFUL BALLOON!

AND YOU'RE ALL MINE.. MINE... MINE....

WHOOPS!

HEY! COME BACK HERE!

COME BACK HERE!

OH, PLEASE COME BACK, BALLOON! PLEASE!

YOU DIRTY OL' BALLOON! COME BACK HERE!!

OH, PLEASE COME BACK... PLEASE.....

YOU DIRTY BALLOON! YOU BETTER COME BACK HERE!!

OH, PLEASE! PLEASE! I'LL DO ANYTHING IF YOU'LL JUST COME BACK

OH, YOU DIRTY BALLOON! IF YOU DON'T COME BACK, I'LL..

OH, PLEASE, BALLOON! OH, PLEASE! OH,..

OH, RATS!
SCHULZ

ONE, TWO, THREE, FOUR, FIVE...

SIXTEEN, SEVENTEEN, EIGHTEEN...

NINETY-ONE
NINETY-TWO

NINETY-THREE
NINETY-FOUR

PUFF PUFF

PUFF PUFF

PANT
PANT

CHOMP! CHOMP!

Allegro
ff
Ped
SCHULZ

LET'S WALK UP TO THE DIME-STORE, LUCY, AND LOOK AT ALL THE TOYS

I THINK IT'S A LOT OF FUN EVEN IF YOU CAN'T BUY ANYTHING

LOOK HERE, LUCY... LOOK AT ALL THE LITTLE DOLLS!
10¢
?
!
15¢

ALL I CAN SEE IS THE FRONT OF THE COUNTER..
AND LOOK OVER HERE...LOOK AT THE TINY DISHES!

I MUST SAY THEY'RE PUTTING GOOD WOOD INTO 'EM THESE DAYS...
GEE...AN' LOOK OVER HERE..

NICE AND SMOOTH, TOO... GOOD JOB OF SANDING
LOOK AT ALL THE PAPER DOLLS...AND LOOK AT THOSE TOY BOATS...

I SEE THEY USED SCREWS INSTEAD OF NAILS...THAT'S A GOOD IDEA...
HERE'RE SOME TINY AIRPLANES, AND THERE'S A TINY FIRE ENGINE!

WE'LL HAVE TO DO THAT AGAIN SOME DAY, HUH, LUCY?
SURE...CALL FOR ME AGAIN IN ABOUT FOUR YEARS!
SCHULZ

?

GROWF!

ARF ARF

ARF!
ARF!
ARF!
ARF!

WHAM!

SCHULZ

POOR OL' 'PIG-PEN'... I'LL BET HE COULD RAISE A CLOUD OF DUST RUNNING ON A SIDEWALK!

HERE, CHARLIE BROWN... I'VE GOT A PIECE OF CANDY FOR YOU..

GEE...I CAN'T GET IT OUT OF MY POCKET.. IT'S STUCK...

THERE!
OH, GOOD GRIEF!

I'LL BRUSH THE LINT OFF FOR YOU,.. AND SCRAPE THIS OLD GUM OFF THE BEST I CAN...
I FEEL SICK

WELL, WHY DON'T YOU EAT IT?
I WILL, 'PIG-PEN', I WILL...I JUST...I.. I..

WHOOPS! I DROPPED IT!
!
GULP!
ZOOM

PSST... SNOOPY, OL' PAL...YOU'D BETTER COME HOME WITH ME, AND HAVE A DRINK OF WATER..
?
SCHULZ

O.K., THAT'S ENOUGH..TURN THE WATER OFF...

IT'S OUR DUTY TO REVIVE FULLY THE LOST ART OF MUD-PIE BAKING

SLOSH THE MUD AROUND REAL GOOD!

NOW, MIX IT UP! STIR IT AROUND! STIR IT AROUND!
I'M STILL SLOSHING!

BOY, LOOK AT THAT TEXTURE!
ISN'T IT WONDERFUL?!

WE'RE THE BEST MUD PIE BAKERS IN THIS WHOLE COUNTRY!
?

WOW! ARE YOU GIRLS EVER A MESS! WAIT UNTIL YOUR MOTHERS SEE YOU!!

WHY? WHAT'S WRONG? WE'VE GOT OUR APRONS ON!
SCHULZ

JANUARY, FEBRUARY, MARCH...

ONE TWO, THREE, FOUR, **FIVE**!

GOOD GRIEF! SPRING BEGAN **FIVE** DAYS AGO!

I GOTTA CALL SCHROEDER...I'LL BET HE DOESN'T EVEN KNOW IT...

WADDYA MEAN, Y'DON'T CARE WHAT THE CALENDAR SAYS?!

BY GOLLY, **I** SURE CARE WHAT THE CALENDAR SAYS!

C'MON! LET'S PLAY BALL!!
SCHULZ

HEY, LOOKIT! LOOK AT ALL THE RECORDS IN THIS BOX!
THEY MUST BELONG TO MY MOTHER AND DAD...

I DIDN'T THINK THEY EVEN HAD PHONOGRAPHS IN THOSE DAYS...

SOME OF THESE OLD RECORDS ARE REALLY FUNNY!

HERE'S ONE CALLED, "OLD ROCKIN' CHAIR'S GOT ME"
PUT IT ON...LET'S LISTEN TO IT

SAY, THAT'S A PRETTY GOOD SONG...

THERE'S ONLY ONE THING I DON'T UNDERSTAND...

WHAT IN THE WORLD IS A "ROCKING CHAIR"?
SCHULZ

WE'VE GOT TO HAVE A RIGHT FIELDER, DON'T WE? GO AHEAD... ASK HER!
I THINK I'D ALMOST RATHER FORFEIT THE GAME!

NO GOOD CAN POSSIBLY COME OF THIS...

LUCY, HOW WOULD YOU LIKE TO BE A SUBSTITUTE?

I DON'T THINK I WOULD... I'VE ALWAYS WANTED TO BE A NURSE

THAT'S NOT WHAT I MEAN... WE'RE SHORT ONE PLAYER... WE NEED YOU FOR RIGHT FIELD
OH..

THE SUN IS PRETTY BRIGHT OUT THERE SO YOU'D BETTER WEAR THESE DARK GLASSES

EVEN THOUGH I DON'T KNOW WHAT'S GOING ON, I FEEL REAL PROFESSIONAL

THESE GLASSES WOULD BE PERFECT IF AN ECLIPSE CAME ALONG..

I'VE NEVER REALLY SEEN AN ECLIPSE..

THERE JUST MIGHT BE ONE ALL READY TO COME ALONG

BONK!

HEY, CHARLIE BROWN!

HERE... TAKE YOUR OL' DARK GLASSES... I THINK THEY'RE BAD FOR MY EYES..

THEY GIVE ME A HEADACHE!

ALL RIGHT, WHO'S GOT MY BALLOON !?!

JUST WAIT UNTIL I CATCH THE PERSON WHO TOOK THAT BALLOON...BOY-O-BOY!!

LINUS, DID YOU SEE WHO TOOK MY BALLOON?!
MMBG

WELL, YOU'RE JUST LUCKY YOU DIDN'T HAVE ANYTHING TO DO WITH IT...

WHEW!
SCHULZ

Pat
Pat
Pat

AH! THE FIRST SNOWBALL OF THE YEAR!

I LIKE TO BEGIN EACH WINTER BY HITTING CHARLIE BROWN RIGHT ON THE HEAD!

I CAN'T DO IT... I CAN'T DO IT...

IT'S NO USE...I JUST CAN'T DO IT...OH, BOO, HOO, HOO...HE'S SO INNOCENT...I JUST CAN'T DO IT..
?
SOB
SOB
SOB

I WAS GOING TO HIT YOU WITH THIS SNOWBALL, CHARLIE BROWN, BUT I'M TOO SOFT-HEARTED...
WELL, I'M GLAD YOU CHANGED YOUR MIND, LUCY...YOU'RE A GOOD GIRL..

WHAT AM I DOING? I'VE GOT TO GET HOLD OF MYSELF!

POW!

OH, IT'S GOING TO BE A GREAT WINTER!
SCHULZ

MERRY 'day after Christmas'! MAY I COME IN?

YOU'LL NEVER BELIEVE THIS I KNOW, BUT I WAS HOPING YOU'D COME OVER..

I WANT YOU TO SEE ALL THE NICE CHRISTMAS PRESENTS I GOT, CHARLIE BROWN..

LOOK! A NEW TOY PIANO!

BLACK KEYS STILL JUST PAINTED ON, I SEE...

A NEW STATUE OF BEETHOVEN..
VERY SCOWLLY..

A NEW BEETHOVEN SWEAT SHIRT...

A BEETHOVEN BALL-POINT PEN...

A TWELVE-VOLUME BIOGRAPHY OF BEETHOVEN IN COMIC-BOOK FORM...

AND A YEAR'S SUPPLY OF BEETHOVEN BUBBLE GUM!

OH, YES ... I ALMOST FORGOT... I ALSO GOT AN ELECTRIC TRAIN..

NOW, WHAT IN THE WORLD AM I GOING TO DO WITH AN ELECTRIC TRAIN?!
SCHULZ

OH, GOOD GRIEF!

WILL YOU READ ME A STORY, CHARLIE BROWN?
I'M TRAPPED... THERE'S NO USE KIDDING MYSELF... I'M TRAPPED...

WON'T YOU **PLEASE** READ ME A STORY, CHARLIE BROWN?

OH, ALL RIGHT... I SUPPOSE WE MIGHT AS WELL GET IT OVER..

LET'S SEE WHAT THEY'VE GOT HERE...

Once upon a time they lived happily ever after. The End.

?

HEY...

WHAT'S ON THE REST OF THESE PAGES.... **ADVERTISING**?
SCHULZ

AS LONG AS I'M AT THIS END OF THE BLOCK, I REALLY OUGHT TO STOP IN AND SEE LINUS AND LUCY..

I HAVEN'T SEEN LINUS FOR QUITE A WHILE...

HOW'S YOUR BABY BROTHER, LUCY ?

I DON'T THINK HE'S VERY WELL... I'M WORRIED ABOUT HIM...

WHY ? HE LOOKS FINE TO ME... IN FACT, HE LOOKS VERY HAPPY

NO, I DON'T THINK SO...WATCH..

HEY, LINUS!

SEE? HE'S AWFULLY NERVOUS!
SCHULZ

THAT'S WHAT I THINK OF YOUR BOX OF COOKIES!
COOKIES

THAT'S WHAT I THINK OF YOUR OL' PIANO!
?

THAT'S WHAT I THINK OF YOUR OL' STAMP COLLECTION!

AND THAT'S WHAT I THINK OF YOUR OL' PICTURE PUZZLE!

AND THAT'S WHAT I THINK OF YOUR STUPID OL' MARBLES!

AND THAT'S WHAT I THINK OF YOUR SILLY OL' COLOR CRAYONS!

SCHULZ
I'M FRUSTRATED AND INHIBITED, AND NOBODY UNDERSTANDS ME..

IT SAYS HERE THAT IF A DOG'S NOSE IS WARM, HE PROBABLY ISN'T FEELING WELL..

VERY INTERESTING...

I WONDER IF SNOOPY'S NOSE IS WARM OR COLD?
WHY DON'T YOU FIND OUT?
?

YOU MEAN TOUCH HIS NOSE?! OH, NO...I COULDN'T DO THAT...OH, NO....I'D BE SCARED...

YOU MEAN WALK RIGHT OVER, AND TOUCH IT, DON'T YOU? OH, NO....I DON'T THINK I COULD EVER.. I'LL DO IT!

NICE DOGGIE...NICE DOGGIE...EASY...EASY NOW.. NICE DOGGIE...EASY..EASY.. EASY..EASY..EASY..
?

AH-CHOO!

HE EXPLODED!
SCHULZ

LUCK!

DUMB LUCK!!
PLUNK!

LUCK!
CLINK!

PLAIN LUCK! JUST PLAIN, DOWNRIGHT, OL' FOOL LUCK!
CLUNK!

LUCK, LUCK, LUCK!
PLINK!

WELL, THAT ENDS THE GAME, CHARLIE BROWN...UNLESS YOU'VE GOT SOME MORE MARBLES...
YOU KNOW I HAVEN'T!

YOU JUST CAN'T BEAT FOOL LUCK!
♪

LUCK! LUCK LUCK! LUCK!

BOY, CAN THAT GIRL EVER PLAY MARBLES!
SCHULZ

I DREAD COMING TO THE CORNER...I KNOW JUST WHAT'S GOING TO HAPPEN..

THE LIFE YOU SAVE MAY BE A FUSSBUDGET..

LET ME HAVE YOUR HAND, LUCY, AS WE CROSS THE STREET..

OH, NO YOU DON'T!

I KNOW YOUR KIND, CHARLIE BROWN! YOU JUST WANT TO HOLD HANDS!
OH, GOOD GRIEF! HERE WE GO AGAIN!

YOU'RE THE MOST AGGRAVATING PERSON IN THE WORLD!!

I DON'T CARE!! I'M NOT GOING TO HOLD HANDS WITH ANY BOY!

ALL RIGHT, GET RUN OVER BY A CAR THEN! CROSS THE STREET BY YOURSELF!!

WAIT A MINUTE, CHARLIE BROWN...
NOW, WHAT?

I'VE GOT AN IDEA...

SCHULZ

?

I DON'T GET IT..
?

?
?

WHY DOES LINUS SIT AROUND ALL DAY HOLDING THAT BLANKET?

IT GIVES HIM SECURITY AND HAPPINESS... DIDN'T YOU HAVE A BLANKET WHEN YOU WERE LITTLE, CHARLIE BROWN?

HERE...FEEL HOW SOFT IT IS...IT'S CALLED 'OUTING' FLANNEL..
OUTING FLANNEL?!

YOU MEAN IF I HOLD THIS NEXT TO MY CHEEK ALL DAY, I'LL BE **HAPPY**?
INSANELY HAPPY!!!

THAT'S THE MOST **STUPID** THING I'VE EVER HEARD!
!

STILL...I COULD USE A LITTLE SECURITY...

ONE YARD OF 'OUTING' FLANNEL.. AND **DON'T LAUGH!!**
DRY GOODS
SCHULZ

WHEW

NERVOUS ENERGY..
CHARLES M. SCHULZ

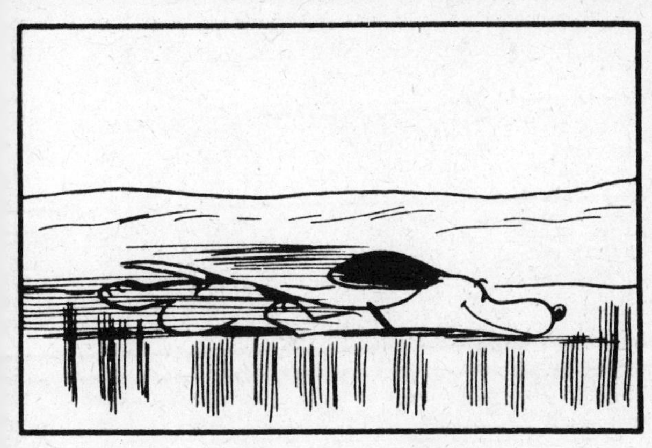

?

!

THAT'S THE WAY IT GOES...
SCHULZ

WELL, I'M UP HERE!

I'VE NEVER TRIED THIS BEFORE, YOU KNOW...

WHAT DO I DO NOW, CHARLIE BROWN?

JUST GIVE YOURSELF A LITTLE SHOVE...
THAT'S THE WAY!

DOWN YOU GO!
FASTER! FASTER!

FASTER! FASTER, LUCY! FASTER!

I DON'T THINK I'M MOVING...

SOME PEOPLE JUST AREN'T ATHLETIC!
I DON'T THINK I'M MOVING AT ALL...
SCHULZ

FACTS ARE FACTS!
PHOOEY!

WHAT DO YOU MEAN, 'PHOOEY'?
JUST WHAT I SAID ...'PHOOEY'

YOU DON'T KNOW WHAT YOU'RE TALKING ABOUT, LUCY!

IS THAT SO?!
YES, THAT'S SO!

HERE COMES CHARLIE BROWN... LET'S SEE WHAT HE THINKS..
WHO CARES WHAT HE THINKS?!

CHARLIE BROWN, WE WANT YOUR OPINION ON SOMETHING...

IS THERE A SANTA CLAUS OR ISN'T THERE A SANTA CLAUS?

I REFUSE TO GET INVOLVED IN A THEOLOGICAL DISCUSSION!
SCHULZ

IT'S GONE!

OF ALL THE NERVE!

LUCY'S TAKEN MY BASEBALL GLOVE AGAIN!

JUST BECAUSE I LEAVE IT ON THE FRONT SIDEWALK EVERY NIGHT, SHE THINKS IT'S PUBLIC PROPERTY!

I'M GOING TO SETTLE THIS ONCE AND FOR ALL...

HEY, YOU!!
THUMP!

?
!
KLOP!

PLUNK!

CLUMP!

OH, DO YOU WANT YOUR GLOVE BACK, CHARLIE BROWN?
NO, YOU MIGHT AS WELL KEEP IT, LUCY.... I'LL PROBABLY NEVER HAVE ANY USE FOR IT AGAIN!
SCHULZ

FROM TWENTY-TWO TO TWENTY-THREE TO TWENTY-FOUR TO TWENTY-FIVE TO TWENTY-SIX TO TWENTY-SEVEN...
?

SEE, LUCY? YOU JUST FOLLOW THE NUMBERS AROUND, AND CONNECT ALL THE DOTS...
AND THERE'S A PICTURE OF A KITTY! WELL, I'LL BE!

I NEVER KNEW THAT JUST CONNECTING DOTS COULD BE SO MUCH FUN..

I DON'T KNOW MUCH ABOUT NUMBERS, BUT I'M **SURE** I CAN CONNECT DOTS!

TUM DE TUM TE DA TE DUM

!

SCHULZ

WELL, THANKS TO THAT LAST STUPID PLAY YOU MADE, I WIN AGAIN!
RATS!

I CAN'T STAND IT...

THAT MAKES SEVEN THOUSAND GAMES IN A ROW, CHARLIE BROWN..

SEVEN THOUSAND?

I CAN'T STAND IT!!!

I'M GOING CRAZY! WHY CAN'T I WIN JUST ONE GAME?

I'M JUST NO GOOD! THAT'S IT! I'M NO GOOD! I'M NO GOOD!

I CAN'T PLAY CHECKERS, I CAN'T PLAY BASEBALL, I CAN'T PLAY FOOTBALL, I CAN'T DO ANYTHING!
THUMP! THUMP!

AND I CAN'T STAND IT!

WHY CAN'T I WIN JUST ONCE?! JUST ONCE?

WELL, ARE YOU BACK TO NORMAL?

YES, I GUESS SO... GO AHEAD..START ANOTHER GAME..
SCHULZ

Hey!

GIMME THOSE TOYS!!!

EVERYTHING'S MINE! MINE! MINE! MINE!
SIGH

HERE...I GUESS YOU CAN HAVE THIS RUBBER BAND... HAVE FUN WITH THAT..

WHAT'S GOING ON HERE?!

GIMME THAT!

I DIDN'T MEAN FOR YOU TO HAVE THAT MUCH FUN!
SCHULZ

ALL OF US GOT NICE THINGS FOR CHRISTMAS EXCEPT HIM..

IT DOESN'T MATTER IF HE'S ONLY A DOG...HE'S OUR FRIEND..

SO YOU SEE, I THOUGHT I'D BETTER TAKE UP A COLLECTION TO GET SNOOPY A LITTLE CHRISTMAS PRESENT..

WHY, HOW NICE!
YES! HOW THOUGHTFUL OF YOU, CHARLIE BROWN!

I'LL BE GLAD TO DONATE A NICKEL...
I WILL, TOO... HERE....

IT'S SO GOOD OF YOU TO BE GOING TO ALL THIS TROUBLE...
YES, AND TO BE TAKING UP YOUR OWN VALUABLE TIME
ALL I HAVE TO DO NOW IS FIND A STORE THAT'S OPEN..

GEE...THOSE GIRLS SURE SAID SOME NICE THINGS...THEY ALWAYS USED TO MAKE ME FEEL SO INFERIOR.. I GUESS THEY DON'T THINK I'M SO BAD AFTER ALL...

BOY, WHAT A DOPE THAT CHARLIE BROWN IS!
YOU CAN SAY THAT AGAIN!
SCHULZ

ARE YOU SURE, CHARLIE BROWN? ARE YOU ABSOLUTELY SURE? ARE YOU?

SIGH

LUCY, WHY DO YOU ASK ME THINGS IF YOU DON'T EVER BELIEVE ME?

OH, I BELIEVE YOU, CHARLIE BROWN..I BELIEVE EVERYTHING YOU TELL ME...

YOU DO NOT!
SURE, I DO... TELL ME SOMETHING, AND WATCH ME BELIEVE YOU..

OH, GOOD GRIEF... DON'T BE SO STUPID!
COME ON...TELL ME SOMETHING...WATCH ME BELIEVE YOU..TELL ME ANYTHING...

THE WORLD IS MADE OF SNOW
I BELIEVE YOU!

THE WORLD IS MADE OF SNOW!!

HEY, VIOLET, CHARLIE BROWN JUST TOLD ME THAT THE WORLD IS MADE OF SNOW..
!
CHARLIE BROWN IS OUT OF HIS MIND!

YOU'RE OUT OF YOUR MIND, CHARLIE BROWN!
SCHULZ

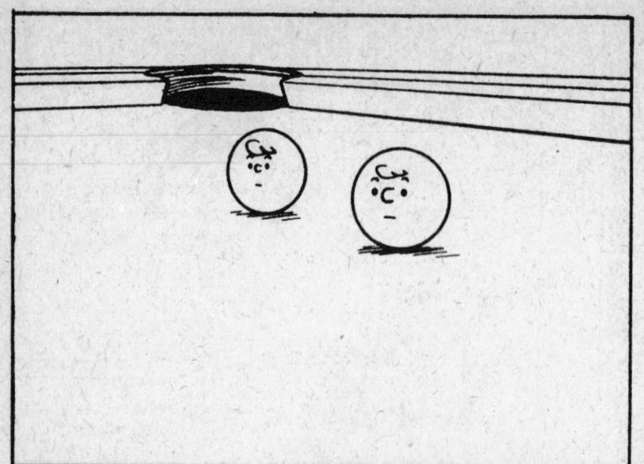

YOU WANT ME TO 'BREAK'?
SURE, GO AHEAD.. LADIES FIRST..
WHERE'S THE CHALK?

WHAT HAPPENS IF I CLEAR THE TABLE?
THEN YOU WIN, OF COURSE..
'CLEAR THE TABLE'.. WHAT A LAUGH!

?!
!

WHAM!!

I CLEARED THE TABLE! I CLEARED THE TABLE! I WON!! I WON!

GOOD GRIEF! WHAT HAPPENED?
I THINK SHE CLEARED THE TABLE...

DON'T GET TOO UPSET, CHARLIE BROWN...MAYBE NEXT WINTER YOU CAN USE IT FOR A SLED!
SCHULZ

BAM!
BAM!

CHARGE!

KAWAM
KAWAM
ZAP!

POW! KAZAAP!!
ZAAP!
?

WUMP! POW! POW!
BAM! BAM! BAM!
KAWOOM!!
KAZAAP!

LUCY, CAN'T YOU AND YOUR FRIENDS PLAY A LITTLE MORE QUIETLY?
ALL RIGHT, MOTHER...

RATTLE
RATTLE

DIDN'T YOU HEAR MOTHER?!
STOP THAT AWFUL NOISE!!
SCHULZ

C'MON, SNOOPY..
C'MON, BOY..

NICE DOGGIE...
NICE SNOOPY..

?

TRY IT.... IT'S AMAZING..

!
I FEEL KIND OF SILLY..

?
SHHH...

YOU'RE RIGHT, LUCY...UH, HUH..

I CAN HEAR THE OCEAN ROAR!
Oh, good grief!!
SCHULZ

NINE HUNDRED AN' ONE..NINE HUNDRED AN' TWO...

SEE, I THOUGHT YOU'D HAVE GIVEN UP BY THIS TIME..
NO, SIR! WHEN I GET STARTED ON SOMETHING REALLY WORTH WHILE I NEVER GIVE UP!

IF YOU'RE GOING TO COUNT ALL THESE STARS, I THINK I'D BETTER HELP YOU..

WELL! I APPRECIATE THIS, CHARLIE BROWN
HAVE YOU COUNTED THAT LITTLE ONE UP THERE?

WHICH LITTLE ONE? THAT ONE?
NO, THAT LITTLE ONE OVER THERE..
OVER THERE?
NO, THERE..

YOU MEAN THAT LITTLE ONE NEXT TO THAT CHARTREUSE ONE?
NO, THAT LITTLE ONE RIGHT THERE
YOU MEAN RIGHT THERE?

NO, RIGHT THERE..RIGHT UP THERE..
THERE? UP THERE?
NO, NO, THERE!
THERE? THERE?
NO! THERE!
THERE?
YES! THERE!

WHAT ABOUT IT?
SCHULZ

ALL YOU HAVE TO DO IS KEEP YOUR EYE ON THE BALL..

GIRLS ARE A NUISANCE SOMETIMES, BUT IT'S ALWAYS A GOOD IDEA TO HUMOR THEM..

O.K., TRY AN' HIT IT..

POW!

KLUNK!

A HOME RUN
OOF!

WELL? DO YOU THINK I'M GOOD ENOUGH TO PLAY ON YOUR TEAM, CHARLIE BROWN?
YOU'LL NEVER PLAY ON MY TEAM!

BUT WHY NOT?
BECAUSE I'M GIVING UP THE GAME..
SCHULZ

BIG KIDS DRIVE ME CRAZY...

WELL, I'LL BE!

I CAN'T BELIEVE IT!

ALL THESE TOYS, AND NOBODY AROUND
NO BIG KIDS TO TAKE THINGS AWAY FROM ME JUST WHEN I'M STARTING TO HAVE FUN...
AC
26
VAN

I CAN'T STAND BIG KIDS..
I CAN'T GET OVER IT.. ALL THESE TOYS AND NOBODY AROUND...
RT

OH, GOOD GRIEF! HERE THEY COME!

BIG KIDS!!

SIGH
SCHULZ

DID YOU KNOW THAT LUCY WAS GOING TO DANCING SCHOOL?
OH HUH... IT'S JUST ONE MORE WAY FOR HER MOTHER TO GET HER OUT OF THE HOUSE...

ASK HER TO DO A FEW STEPS FOR US..

HOW'S DANCING SCHOOL, LUCY?
FINE!

HOW ABOUT SHOWING US WHAT YOU'VE LEARNED?
WELL ...I'M NOT SURE I CAN REMEMBER EVERYTHING, BUT...

SCHULZ
THAT COST MY DAD TWELVE DOLLARS!

I APPRECIATE YOUR COMING OVER TO HELP ME, CHARLIE BROWN...

THE FIRST THING WE DO IS GET YOU A STOOL TO SIT ON..
?

THIS IS SOMETHING I LEARNED FROM VIRGIL THOMSON

YOU SIT RIGHT THERE, SEE, AND THEN I'LL PAINT YOUR MUSICAL PORTRAIT..
OH, I GET IT..YOU'LL TRY TO CAPTURE MY PERSONALITY IN MUSIC...RIGHT?

RIGHT...ARE YOU READY?
I'M READY...THIS IS VERY FLATTERING..

MINE IS THE TYPE OF PERSONALITY THAT WILL PROBABLY INSPIRE AN HEROIC SYMPHONY...

?

I DON'T HEAR A THING...

!

SIGH
SCHULZ

Z

GIMME THAT BLANKET!

WHEW

?

SCHULZ

?

THERE...NOW WE'RE ALL SET...

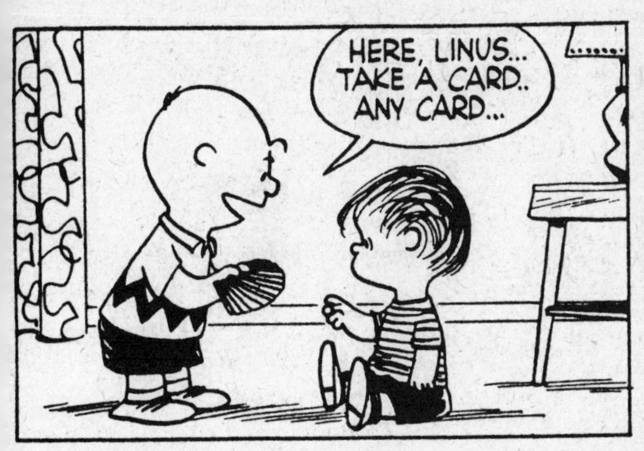
HERE, LINUS... TAKE A CARD.. ANY CARD...

NOW, I'M GOING TO SHOW YOU A LITTLE....A...A... I'M...I'M.....

HERE...TAKE A CARD...ANY CARD..
SCHULZ

MAN! THAT KITE IS REALLY UP THERE!!

LOOK, SCHROEDER...HAVE YOU EVER SEEN A KITE UP SO HIGH?

I'VE GOT TO HAND IT TO YOU, LUCY...I ALWAYS THOUGHT YOU WERE KIND OF DUMB BUT ANYONE WHO CAN GET A KITE UP THAT HIGH IS ALL RIGHT IN MY BOOK! YES, SIR!

GOING TO HAUL IT IN NOW EH? THAT'S PROBABLY A GOOD IDEA...A KITE SHOULDN'T BE KEPT UP IN THE AIR TOO LONG...ESPECIALLY ONE THAT WAS THAT HIGH...

?
?

SCHULZ

I THOUGHT I HEARD HOOFBEATS?

LOOK OUT! HERE HE COMES AGAIN!!

GOOD GRIEF!?
ZOOM!

!
!
ZOOM!

ZOOM!

NO, NO, SNOOPY! NOT THOSE!!

WHAM!

SCHULZ
BOY, WHAT A STUPID DOG!

SIGH!

AH HA HA HA!
HO HO HO!
!

BONK!
SCHULZ

HI, FUSSBUDGET... IS LINUS HOME?
HE'S IN THE OTHER ROOM..

IS THAT A BALL, OR ARE YOU CARRYING YOUR HEAD UNDER YOUR ARM?
WHY DON'T YOU GO THROW YOURSELF ON THE FLOOR, FUSSBUDGET?

EVER SEEN A BASKETBALL, BEFORE, LINUS?

BASKETBALL IS A GREAT GAME, I TELL YOU! A PERFECT COMBINATION OF SPEED AND SKILL, AND...

!

BUMPETY BUMPETY BUMPETY
BUMP BUMP
BUMPETY bumpety BUMPETY BUMPETY bumpety bumpety
Bumpety BUMPETY BUMPETY bumpety BUMPETY BUMPETY BUMP BOMP

SWISH!
THUMP
PLUNK!

THERE'S NOTHING MORE ANNOYING THAN A SMART-ALECKY KID!
SCHULZ

HEY! COME BACK HERE!

HE'S GOT OUR BALL AGAIN!
SNOOPY!

YOU COME BACK HERE WITH THAT BALL!!

YOU CRAZY DOG!
LOOK WHERE HE WENT! NOW WE'LL NEVER GET HIM!

SNOOPY'S GOT OUR BALL, AND WON'T GIVE IT BACK TO US..
HE WON'T, EH? WHERE IS HE?
HE'S SITTING OVER THERE IN THE MIDDLE OF THE YARD

IN THE MIDDLE OF THE YARD?! THEN WHY DON'T YOU JUST GO TAKE IT? HE WON'T BITE...
WE CAN'T.. WE JUST CAN'T..
YOU DON'T UNDER-STAND...

I DON'T SEE WHY YOU CAN'T TAKE A BALL FROM A DOG WHO WON'T BITE AND IS JUST SITTING IN THE MIDDLE OF THE YARD...

OH...
SCHULZ

WHAP!

WHOP!

WHANG!

ALL RIGHT... I'VE GOT IT UP HERE AS FAR AS THE NET...NOW WHAT?
SCHULZ

WATCH ME HIT THAT TREE SNOOPY..

?
?

PLOP!

YOU GOT IN THE WAY!
SCHULZ

ARE YOU READY?

HERE WE GO!!

HANG ON!

DOWN! DOWN! DOWN!

RACING LIKE THE WIND...

WE MADE IT !!
!

SHALL WE TRY IT AGAIN RIGHT AWAY, OR DO YOU WANT TO WAIT UNTIL YOU CATCH YOUR BREATH?
SCHULZ

POOF!

WHOP!

BASEBALL IS NO LONGER A HITTER'S GAME..
SCHULZ

Joker
Joker

WATCH ME, LINUS, AND I'LL SHOW YOU HOW TO BUILD A HOUSE OF CARDS...

IT'S KIND OF HARD AT FIRST, BUT AFTER YOU CATCH ON, IT...RATS!

C'MON! STAND UP THERE..RATS! C'MON, NOW...THAT'S THE WAY..RATS! RATS! RATS!

STEADY...STEADDY.. STEAAADDDDY...

There! How's THAT !?

!
SCHULZ

I CAN'T STAND SMART-ALECKY KIDS!

SIX HUNDRED! AN ALL-TIME RECORD!

WHEEEEEEEE

NOBODY CAN JUMP ROPE BETTER THAN I!

NOBODY! NOBODY! NOBODY!

I'M THE BEST THERE IS! THE BEST, THE BEST, THE VERY BEST..

?
SIX HUNDRED AN NINETY EIGHT.. SIX HUNDRED AN' NINETY NINE.. SEVEN HUNDRED.. SEVEN HUNDRED AN' ONE.. SEVEN HUNDRED AN' TWO..

!
SEVEN HUNDRED AN' THREE.. SEVEN HUNDRED AN' FOUR..

MY OWN BABY BROTHER...
SCHULZ

COOKIES

CHOMP CHOMP
COOKIES

CHOMP CHOMP CHOMP
COOKIES

CHOMP CHOMP
COOKIES

CHOMP CHOMP CHOMP
COOKIES

CHOMP CHOMP CHOMP
COOKIES

CHOMP CHOMP

GRROWRRRRRRR
CHOMP CHOMP

SIGH
CHOMP CHOMP CHOMP
SCHULZ

HEY!

COME BACK HERE!

PATTY, HAVE YOU SEEN MY PLASTIC SWIMMING POOL? I WAS JUST GOING TO FILL IT WITH WATER WHEN THE WIND BLEW IT AWAY..

'FLYING SAUCERS ARE REAL,' IT SAYS HERE... 'AUTHENTIC REPORTS INDICATE'..

AAK!

THEY GOT ME! THEY GOT ME!
?

HELP!
RIP!

A MARTIAN!

HE POINTED HIS FLAME-THROWER RIGHT AT ME!
ONE NEW SWIMMING POOL.. COMPLETELY SHOT!
SCHULZ

HE'S SO CUTE... SIGH

I'LL BET IF WE WERE TO GET MARRIED SOME DAY, SCHROEDER, WE'D BE VERY HAPPY...

WHILE YOU WERE PRACTICING THE PIANO, I'D BE IN THE KITCHEN MAKING YOUR BREAKFAST...

THEN I'D BRING IT IN LIKE THIS, AND SET IT ALL OUT NICE, AND PROP UP YOUR FAVORITE NEWS-PAPER, AND POUR YOUR COFFEE...

WOULDN'T THAT BE ROMANTIC?

MUSICIANS AREN'T REAL PEOPLE!
SCHULZ

GEE, IT'S COLD IN HERE...

SOMETIMES I THINK I'D LIKE TO BE ALMOST ANYTHING BUT A DOG..

BIRDS ARE THE PEOPLE I ENVY THE MOST...

BOY! THERE'S THE LIFE!

SIGH!

?

SCHULZ

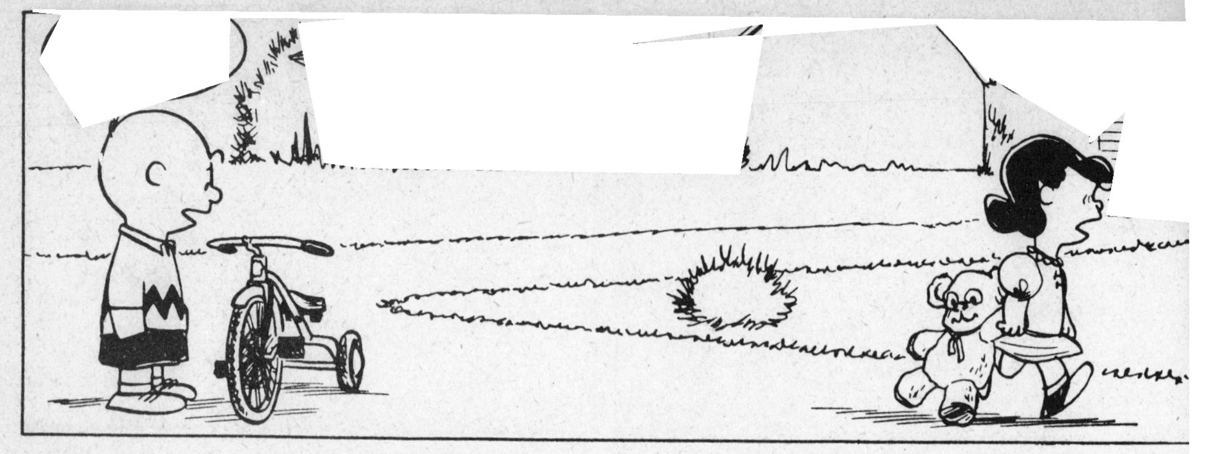

DOES THIS BELONG TO LINUS, TOO?
SURE..

AND LOOK AT THIS NICE CAR...HE GOT THAT FOR HIS BIRTHDAY...
WOW!
Chain Drive

COME ON IN THE HOUSE...I'LL SHOW YOU A FEW OTHER THINGS...

SEE? HE HAS GAMES, BOOKS, RECORDS....EVERYTHING!

SO YOU KNOW WHAT HE PLAYS WITH ALL DAY LONG?

THE VACUUM CLEANER!
SCHULZ

?

SCHULZ

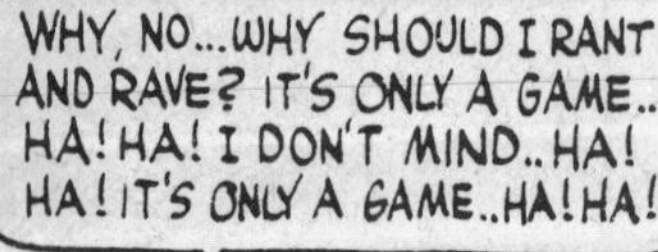

BUT I CAN'T STAND PLAYING WITH A GOOD LOSER!